FOUNDATIONS OF MODERN ANTHROPOLOGY SERIES

Marshall D. Sahlins, *Editor*

FOUNDATIONS OF MODERN ANTHROPOLOGY SERIES

PRENTICE-HALL, INC., Englewood Cliffs, New Jersey

C. Loring Brace, University of Michigan

The Stages

of Human Evolution

HUMAN AND CULTURAL ORIGINS

PRENTICE-HALL

FOUNDATIONS OF MODERN ANTHROPOLOGY SERIES

Marshall D. Sahlins, *Editor*

Current printing (last digit):
10 9 8 7 6 5 4 3 2 1

PRENTICE-HALL INTERNATIONAL, INC., *London*
PRENTICE-HALL OF AUSTRALIA, PTY., LTD., *Sydney*
PRENTICE-HALL OF CANADA, LTD., *Toronto*
PRENTICE-HALL OF INDIA PVT. LTD., *New Delhi*
PRENTICE-HALL OF JAPAN, INC., *Tokyo*

Foundations

of Modern Anthropology

Series

The Foundations of Modern Anthropology Series is a documentation of the human condition, past and present. It is concerned mainly with exotic peoples, prehistoric times, unwritten languages, and unlikely customs. But this is merely the anthropologist's way of expressing his concern for the here and now, and his way makes a unique contribution to our knowledge of what's going on in the world. We cannot understand ourselves apart from an understanding of *man*, nor our culture apart from an understanding of *culture*. Inevitably we are impelled toward an intellectual encounter with man in all his varieties, no matter how primitive, how ancient, or how seemingly insignificant. Ever since their discovery by an expanding European civilization, primitive peoples have continued to hover over thoughtful men like ancestral ghosts, ever provoking this anthropological curiosity. To "return to the primitive" just for what it is would be foolish; the savage is not nature's nobleman and his existence is no halcyon idyll. For anthropology, the romance of the primitive has been something else:

v

a search for the roots and meaning of ourselves—in the context of all mankind.

The series, then, is designed to display the varieties of man and culture and the evolution of man and culture. All fields of anthropology are relevant to the grand design and all of them—prehistoric archaeology, physical anthropology, linguistics, and ethnology (cultural anthropology)—are represented among the authors of the several books in the series. In the area of physical anthropology are books describing the early condition of humanity and the subhuman primate antecedents. The later development of man on the biological side is set out in the volume on races, while the archaeological accounts of the Old World and the New document development on the historical side. Then there are the studies of contemporary culture, including a book on how to understand it all—i.e., on ethnological theory—and one on language, the peculiar human gift responsible for it all. Main types of culture are laid out in "The Hunters," "Tribesmen," "Formation of the State," and "Peasants." Initiating a dialogue between contemplation of the primitive and the present, the volume on "The Present as Anthropology" keeps faith with the promise of anthropological study stated long ago by E. B. Tylor, who saw in it "the means of understanding our own lives and our place in the world, vaguely and imperfectly it is true, but at any rate more clearly than any former generation."

Looked at from this point of view, the Neanderthal and Pithecanthropus skulls stand like the piers of a ruined bridge which once continuously connected the kingdom of man with the rest of the animal world.

William J. Sollas

Preface

Of all the subjects that have provoked the play of human curiosity, man's concern with his own prehistoric origins has few equals. At the same time, few subjects have been the target for so much unprofessional speculation; and while the present work aims at no reduction in the quantity of speculations (quite the reverse), it is the hope of the author that they can, technically at least, bear the label of *professional* speculations. Part of the reason for the less-than-abundant work on human origins is that, in this material world, it can produce little measurable gain. Physics can produce bigger and more expensive explosions, basic biology has its medical consequences, and such subjects as geology and economics contribute to man's mineral and monetary well-being, but prehistoric anthropology can reveal only the humble nature of human beginnings, and thus has dubious value as a marketable commodity. Many have regarded it as an interesting hobby, but few have been tempted to treat it as a serious career and devote lifelong concentration to its advancement. Even among the professional practitioners, the competition to qualify is often less severe than is true for other fields, with the result that advances and accomplishments have been far less spectacular than has been the case with, for instance, genetics or electronics. The subject is fascinating, nevertheless, and, for the professionals, it is quite satisfying in and of itself. It is the purpose of the present volume to communicate a modicum of this interest to the reader young or old; perhaps to kindle the spark of what might grow to be another professional career; and to add a possible modifying influence, however minor, to the understandable human tendency to magnify man's present accomplishments to the point where we are inclined to forget how precarious was the very existence of our predecessors until the recent past—and perhaps may again be in the immediate future.

C. Loring Brace

Contents

PART ONE *Discovering the Evidence*

One *Interpreting Human Evolution*

Few educated men and no serious scholars doubt that man has evolved by natural means from a creature which today would not be considered man. From this initial point of agreement, the thinking of those who are considered qualified to judge diverges to such a degree that many feel we do not have a basis which is adequate enough to warrant any interpretation at all. Yet schemes have been constructed which attempt to arrange the prehistoric evidence and account for the course of human evolution, and, in the pages that follow, several of these will be mentioned and a declaration will be made for one of them.

Since it is generally agreed that evolutionary thinking should be applied to the course of prehistoric human development, it would seem unnecessary at first glance to consider the nonevolutionary or even antievolutionary views of pre-Darwinian thought. Further investigation, however, reveals that the difference between several of the attitudes discernible at the present time can in part be traced to the lingering influence of a current of thought which has specific pre-Darwinian sources. Once this has been

3

identified and the historical connections have been traced, then the reason for the differences between the major opposed interpretations will become obvious and we shall have some basis for making a choice between them.

Basically there are two polar and opposed approaches to interpreting the human fossil record. On the one hand, there is the school which takes all the known hominid fossils, arranges them in a lineal sequence, and declares that this is the course which human evolution has pursued. On the other hand, there is the school which declares that the course of evolution is never in a straight, unbranching line—witness the diversity of related forms in the organic world today—and that one should expect to find branches and specializations among human fossils. This latter view tends to regard the differing fossil men as "specializations" away from the main line of human evolution which eventually became extinct without issue.

People invariably are fascinated by the investigation of the skeletons in their closets, and in the field of human evolution one could say that this is literally the case. This fascination has led many people, amateur and professional, to write about fossil man—people who have not been fully qualified and who have failed to perceive the nature of the two schemes just mentioned. As a result many authors prefer a hazy middle ground. Many qualified professionals also prefer the middle course, since they feel that both schemes have some merit, and the result is that only a few authors today represent the poles in fully developed form. In this book, one of the extreme positions will be developed—the linear scheme mentioned above—not because there is conclusive proof for it, but because this is the most consistent means by which the data can be accommodated by the various theoretical frameworks which have been developing in the science of man, and which have been established in related sciences of greater age.

More of this later, but first it should be instructive to sample the various other current views on the course of human evolution. First among these and generally regarded as most traditional is the view that the various different forms in the human fossil record are the results of the adaptive radiation of the basic human line. At present, there are three versions being offered; one which treats the entire human fossil record as a picture of divergent "specialized" lines; another which concentrates on the earlier parts of the record where the human affinities of the forms discovered are less readily apparent; and a third which accepts the available evidence as indicative of the course of human evolution, excepting only the Neanderthals, which alone can be considered "specialized" side lines.

To understand these applications and the criticisms which can be made of them, it is first necessary to gain some sort of perspective of the time scale involved, the fossils concerned, and the principles invoked. Briefly, it has become apparent that the span during which the events of human evolution have occurred was *not* just 300,000 or 800,000 years, as used to be believed, but somewhere in the neighborhood of 2 million years in duration. Previous estimates were based largely upon guesswork involving sedimentation rates and strata thicknesses, but this recent reappraisal is derived from the work of geophysicists who have utilized the known and constant rate of decay of Potassium 40 into Argon. The Potassium-Argon (K/A) proportion in ancient volcanics is directly related to the length of time since they have cooled, and while there are many pitfalls connected with the use of this technique to date strata in the recent past (2 million years is dewy fresh in the full perspective of geological time), it is becoming increasingly apparent that the duration of human existence has been sufficient so that one need not invoke an unusual rate of evolution to account for all the changes which the human fossil record reveals.

The geological period during which man did most of his evolving is called the Pleistocene, and it extended from about 2 million years ago to 10,000 years ago, if indeed it can properly be considered ended. The oldest fossil relatives of man are found in the early Pleistocene and are referred to as **Australopithecines.** These come in two versions, a little one half the size of modern man, and a big one of approximately the same bulk as ourselves. The little Australopithecines appear to be earlier than the big ones, although the evidence is not clear. Aside from gross size, the most evident points of distinction between the Australopithecines and modern man are in the head and face. Simply stated, the head is smaller—brain size is scarcely more than a third that of the modern mean—while the face and teeth are enormous. At the moment, there is a healthy professional brawl going on over the relationship of the early Australopithecines to the late ones, and the significance of both to the total picture of human evolution. A solution to the controversy will be suggested later on in this book, but for now this initial brief sketch is offered so that the reader will have some framework on which he can arrange the arguments that follow.

In the middle of the Pleistocene some half a million years ago there is another cluster of hominid fossils which can be called **Pithecanthropines.** In the upper Pleistocene immediately prior to the appearance of men of recognizably modern form, there is a fossil group which has been called the **Neanderthals.** To be sure, there are other fossils unevenly scattered, in both the geographical and temporal sense, which provide a source for much of the disagreement which still surrounds any attempt to develop a systematic view of human evolution, but the foregoing should provide a useful outline to remember while the discovery of the human fossil record is being recounted.

The scheme which will be developed in later chapters essentially takes these major blocks of fossil hominids, arranges them in temporal sequence, and explores the evolutionary logic whereby the earlier evolved into the later ones. It is these major groups which form the evolutionary stages through which it is claimed that the human line passed. Yet it should also be remembered that the identification of these supposed "stages" is largely dependent upon the accident of discovery. A few rich sites have provided concentrated evidence for particular forms of fossil men, and it is not only possible but extremely likely that had these rich sites involved different time levels, then the identification and number of important stages in human evolution would have been rather different. On the other hand, the present stages perceived are adequate to represent the changes involved, and their consideration can be justified in terms of their utility.

Ultimately, when the entire time spectrum of human existence is documented by an as-yet-unforseeable abundance of fossil evidence, the picture should be one of a completely gradual continuum of accumulating change, with no visible breaks between what are here considered as stages. Human evolution *has* been continual; it continues in the present, and will continue in the future, but our concern in this book is the changes which have taken place in the past.

Two *Fact and Fancy*

before 1860

The earliest recognition of a fossil human was accorded a skull fragment discovered in the year 1700 at Canstatt, near Stuttgart in western Germany. At this early date, however, there was not even the remotest suspicion that modern living forms, including man, might have evolved by natural means from earlier forms ultimately quite different in appearance. Nor was there any faint hint of the vistas of geological antiquity which research was to reveal in the subsequent century. The Canstatt skull was accepted by some as evidence for human existence in ancient times, but its form was not different from that of modern man, and "ancient times" were measured in terms of a total span since creation—thought to be somewhat less than 6,000 years. As late as the middle of the seventeenth century, the vision of such antiquity was considered somewhat daring, although it had received a certain amount of religious sanction in the work of the biblical scholar James Ussher, Archbishop of Armagh. Computing from the named generations recorded in the Bible, Ussher arrived at the conclusion that creation had occurred in the year 4004 B.C. To this, the

Reverend Dr. John Lightfoot, vice-chancellor of Cambridge University, added the pronouncement that ". . . heaven and earth, centre and circumference, were created all together in the same instant, and clouds full of water. This work took place and man was created by the Trinity on October 23, 4004 B.C. at nine o'clock in the morning."

By the end of the eighteenth century, appraisals of geological processes and accumulating knowledge of the structure and strata of the earth led to the suspicion, on the part of some people, that the earth was really very much older. Fossil remains of extinct and different animals had been discovered, and scholars were becoming aware that the world had been a very different place in ages gone by, and that great changes had occurred. A few people even noted that the shaped pieces of flint discovered in prehistoric strata might be the tools of early men before the discovery of metallurgy, and certainly historians and students of human institutions were aware that the world of man had changed even in the recent past.

Early in the nineteenth century, the French biologist Lamarck tried to promote a view according to which continuous and accumulating change was the normal state of affairs. He was really the first thoroughgoing evolutionist, but the mechanism which he proposed to account for organic change was incorrect and his position has been generally rejected. The initial reason for this rejection was the fact that many people were emotionally unprepared to accept change as normal. The traditional view that the world was created fixed and changeless had both social and religious support, and a scheme proposing the normality of constant change was regarded as a threat to the established order. Yet change could be seen in the geological record of the remote past, and some sort of explanation was demanded.

An acceptable solution was proposed by another French scholar, Georges Cuvier, who was a younger contemporary of Lamarck. Cuvier's scheme has been called **catastrophism**. It claimed that the various geological layers had been deposited as the result of a series of cataclysms which had overwhelmed the planet periodically, extinguishing all previously living organisms. The last of these cataclysms, according to Cuvier, was the Biblical flood, which meant that human remains should not be discoverable in previous layers. Cuvier is credited with the statement: "Fossil man does not exist." And indeed, in the early nineteenth century there was very little known evidence to contradict such a position.

Cuvier was somewhat vague concerning the origin of the new animals which appeared in the strata overlying his various supposed cataclysms. Not only did he suggest that they might have migrated into the area concerned from other parts of the world which had not been affected by the regional catastrophe, but he also gave support to a philosophy of successive

Georges Cuvier (1769–1832), zoologist, comparative anatomist, paleontologist, and unwitting influence on many of the subsequent attempts to interpret the human fossil record. (Brown Brothers.)

creations. With the development of Darwinian evolutionary theory in the middle of the nineteenth century, the view of supernaturally caused extinctions, migrations, invasions, and successive creations was superseded as a general explanation. Yet, because of a variety of historical accidents, something of this has survived into the present, at least where considerations of human origins are concerned.

The discovery of the fossil and the archaeological evidence for human evolution was the result of the field work of people who had very little concern for the research which developed the evolutionary explanation for the origin of organic diversity and organic change, yet both realms of activity have parallel careers extending back into the eighteenth century. Archaeological and paleontological work could and did go on without much concern for theoretical implications. Cuvier, in spite of being specifically opposed to evolution, can be regarded as the founder of **paleontology,** a discipline which, ironically, provides the most direct evidence in support of evolutionary theory. His intellectual descendants (and other, unrelated, antiquarians and archaeologists) pursued their diggings right up into the twentieth century, with often quite incorrect assumptions concerning their interpretations. Darwin, on the other hand, used relatively little paleontological evidence to support his major insights. This was partly because of the very incomplete nature of knowledge concerning the

9

fossil record, and partly because his concern was focussed on the attempt to explain diversity in the world of *living* organisms.

Although it has remained for the twentieth century to attempt the thorough synthesis of these two areas of endeavor, scholars in both areas have not been unaware of the implications each has had for the other, and the public has been sensitive to this from the beginning. This still shows in the common misconception concerning the title of Darwin's most famous book, *On the Origin of Species*. From the time of its appearance right up to the present, people who are not thoroughly familiar with it have assumed that it suggests a common ancestry for apes and men, and that the "species" in the title refers to man himself. This latter assumption is so strong that the title is frequently misquoted, being rendered as *The Origin of "The" Species*. Actually, only one brief sentence at the very end makes any reference to man at all, and this is thoroughly noncommittal. Darwin's concern for human evolution was reserved for expression in another book, *The Descent of Man*, published more than a decade after his *Origin*. Even here, however, his reference to the skimpy fossil and archaeological record of human prehistoric existence is brief in the extreme.

The trickle of accumulating evidence had been growing, however, with prehistoric skeletons and stone tools being brought forth even during the lifetime of Cuvier. During the 1820's, human skeletal material was discovered in association with extinct animals and ancient stone tools on the coast of Wales, in France, and in Belgium, but none of it attracted much attention. Late in the 1840's, Boucher de Perthes, a customs inspector at Abbeville in northwestern France, published the results of his prehistoric investigations of the previous 15 years. In the gravel of the Somme river terraces he had discovered flints of such a regular shape that they could only be the products of human manufacture. Yet they obviously were deposited during the course of the formation of the terraces where they were found, which suggested an age for their makers far in excess of anything granted by even the most liberal supporters of human antiquity.

Just a year later, in 1848, a skull was found in a quarry on the north face of the Rock of Gibraltar; this skull we now recognize as a representative of the Neanderthal stage of human evolution. The discovery was recorded by the Gibraltar Scientific Society. A slow 14 years later, after the skull had found its way to England, it was shown to at best mildly interested scholars at meetings of the British Association for the Advancement of Science, and at an anthropological congress. Just 20 years after its discovery it was presented, pretty much as a curiosity piece, to the Museum of the Royal College of Surgeons in London, where it remained, almost forgotten, until after the turn of the century. Since its importance went unappreciated for more than half a century following its exhumation, it

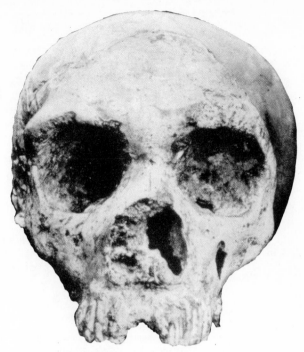

The Gibraltar discovery, a skull of Neanderthal form. (Courtesy of the American Museum of Natural History.)

played no part in the development of the study of human evolution.

This was very nearly the fate of the archaeological discoveries of Boucher de Perthes. Contemporary French scholars were so scornful of his claims that they never even bothered to visit his diggings or investigate his work firsthand, simply remaining in Paris and denouncing from a distance. Had it not been for the curiosity of a group of English scientists, his finds would have had as little influence on the study of human origins as had the Gibraltar skull.

By a remarkable set of historical coincidences, the late 1850's saw the discovery of the skeletal remains of what could be identified as an earlier stage in human evolution, the recognition of the archaeological evidence for human antiquity, and the development of an intellectual framework within which these new facts could be encompassed. The specific timing of these events was a little less fortunte, since the discovery of the skeletal remains occurred first, and they were the subject of sceptical comments which have influenced interpretations ever since. The skeleton was discovered in 1856 during quarry operations in a limestone gorge through which flows the Dussel, a tributary of the lower Rhine. The gorge lies in the area between Elberfeld and Dusseldorf and bears the name of Neanderthal. By giving its name to the skeleton discovered there, it has provided a designation for the entire stage of evolutionary development immediately prior to the emergence of men of modern form.

The skeleton had evidently been a burial in a small cave in the lime-

11

stone cliffs, and had probably been complete. In the course of being recovered it was somewhat battered, since it, along with the dirt in which it lay, was unceremoniously shovelled out onto the terrace by quarry workers who were cleaning out the cave to get at the rock. Its human nature was later recognized by Johann Karl Fuhlrott, a natural science teacher at the high school in Elberfeld, who assured its preservation. Fuhlrott, with the aid of Hermann Schaaffhausen, a professor of anatomy at Bonn, promoted the view that this was an early form of man, but their interpretation received no support until very nearly the end of the nineteenth century. Possibly because of the mode of excavation the face was not recovered—the head being represented by the skull cap from the ridges over the eye sockets on to the back of the skull but minus the base. The limb bones were extraordinarily robust and the brow ridges of the skull enormous, but, lacking the face, jaws, and teeth, the evidence for clear difference from modern man was subject to debate.

And debate there was. Enough peculiarities were present to suggest all sorts of explanations, from hints that it was an ancient Celt of "low type" similar to the modern Irish, to suggestions that it was an idiot, a freak, the victim of rickets, or the residue of the Mongolian Cossacks who had chased Napoleon back from Russia in 1814. The most authoritative opin-

Charles R. Darwin (1809–1882), author of The Origin of Species *and acknowledged father of evolutionary thinking. (National Portrait Gallery, London.)*

ion was delivered by one of Germany's leading scientists, Rudolf Virchow, a founder of German anthropology and, as the originator of the field of cellular pathology, the most outstanding pathologist of the day. After careful examination, he pronounced it pathological and sought to explain all of its peculiarities in that fashion. The weight of his judgment has been such that Neanderthal morpholoy has been regarded as "aberrant" from that day to this, and a majority of authorities even today refuse to accept Neanderthals as representative of the ancestors of modern man.

In 1858, the year following the first discussion of the Neanderthal discovery, a delegation from the Royal Society of Great Britain visited the excavations of Boucher de Perthes in northern France and returned, convinced of the significance of his work, to report to the British scientific world. Then in 1859 Darwin's work *On the Origin of Species* appeared. From then on, man's attitude toward the world of nature and his own position within it was permanently altered: no longer could man regard himself as the epitome of existence in a world created for his own benefit. Of course for quite some time, in the pride of their self-importance, many people could not accept the implications of this presentation. However, as time went on and acceptance became nearly universal, it became apparent that the consequent enforced humility was doing people no harm. The upshot of the entire matter is that no area of human behavior and philosophy has escaped the impact of the consequent revolution in attitudes.

Three   The Picture
up to 1906

The vindication of Boucher de Perthes and the intellectual revolution going on in Britain could not fail to be a great stimulus to prehistoric research. During the late 1850's and 1860's basic work on discovering the characteristics of human cultures prior to the existence of metal was undertaken. In France, particularly in the Dordogne region, and the Vézère river valley of the southwest, excavations at La Madeleine, Solutré, Aurignac, and Le Moustier revealed stone tool-making traditions. These were named **Magdalenian, Solutrean, Aurignacian,** and **Mousterian,** and are now known to be roughly 20, 25, 30, and 40 thousand years old, respectively. It was suspected that these dated from a period more recent than those discovered by Boucher de Perthes; no one then imagined that the difference was actually more than 100,000 years. Then, most exciting of all, in 1868, human skeletal remains were discovered in the same stratigraphic layer with tools of Aurignacian type. To the interest as well as the relief of the public, these remains indicated that the individuals in question were not markedly different from modern man. In fact, their form

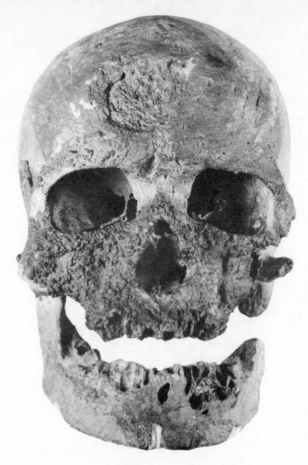

The male Cro-Magnon, from Les Eyzies, Dordogne, France. (Courtesy of the Musée de l'Homme, Paris.)

has been portrayed with a glowing enthusiasm not entirely warranted by their somewhat fragmentary condition.

The human skeletal remains we have been discussing, representing some five individuals, were discovered during the course of constructing the railroad through Les Eyzies, in the aforementioned Dordogne department of southwestern France. The removal of fill for the abutments of the railway bridge revealed a long-hidden rock shelter near an eminence called **Cro-Magnon,** within which the skeletons and artifacts were found. Competent geologists were on hand to verify the antiquity and the stratigraphic associations, and the study of fossil man was finally given its first solidly documented specimens. Stature of the male skeleton can be computed to be 5′ 10″ or 5′ 11″, which is tall in comparison to present or previous world-wide standards, and the rugged, long bones suggest a robust and muscular people. The face was vertical rather than projecting, and possessed a prominent chin, although these features have been stressed to a greater extent than the evidence warrants, in light of the fact that the large male cranium was toothless at discovery.

16

Still, the Cro-Magnon finds were recognizably of modern form, and provide the basis for the still valid assertion that the Upper Palaeolithic tool-making traditions—Aurignacian, Solutrean, Magdalenian, and others —were the products of people not unlike ourselves. Associated art work in the form of carvings and engravings on bone and ivory revealed a degree of sophistication in these Upper Pleistocene hunters which was quite gratifying from the point of view of the people who were beginning to accept these Upper Palaeolithic people as ancestral to more recent men. The decades which followed witnessed the discovery of abundant additional support for the picture outlined in the discoveries at Cro-Magnon, and it was some time before the unearthing of more ancient remains again forced people to face the issues of human evolution—the possibility that man has arisen from something which is different from his present form.

Exactly 30 years after the original discovery in the Neanderthal, and long enough for the controversy to have died down, two human skeletons were found buried in a Mousterian level in a cave in the commune of Spy (pronounced Spee) in the province of Numur, Belgium. The form of both skeletons was recognizably similar to that of the original Neanderthal, and the skull Spy I was of practically the identical shape. No longer was it possible to expound with such certainty the supposed pathological features of the individual from the Neanderthal. However, the adamant Virchow refused to back down and, although the Spy discoveries confirmed the Neanderthal as a type of man, the implications of abnormality and peculiarity tended to remain; indeed, to this day they have not been fully shaken off. Nevertheless, the Neanderthals could now be regarded as a type, associated with a definite tool-making tradition, and given a definite age.

The scene was shortly to shift to another part of the world and involve another, and possibly even more dramatic, form of fossil man. The German naturalist Ernst Haeckel, greatly excited by the implications of Charles Darwin's work, was communicating his enthusiasm for the evolutionary viewpoint to a rising generation of students on the German academic scene. Pushing evolutionary logic to its conclusion, Haeckel drew a hypothetical family tree linking modern man to a common ancestry with the living apes and monkeys. He further suggested that somewhere in between the two, back in the remote past, there must have been a form which was neither one nor the other—a completely transitional stage. This he suggested should be referred to as *Pithecanthropus alalus*, i.e. Ape-man without speech. An American journalist was later to christen this the "missing link," a term which remains as a firm item of popular folklore. Whereas Darwin had suggested that Africa was the most likely place to search for man's earliest ancestor, believing that the gorilla and the chimpanzee were man's closest living relatives, Haeckel and others in Germany stressed southeast Asia, since they claimed that the detailed morphology of the gibbon's skull was more like that of man than was that of the African anthropoid apes. Today, it appears that Darwin's suspicions were the sounder, although the discoveries of the 1890's made Haeckel's guess seem little short of inspired.

Fascinated by Haeckel's portrayal of the hypothetical ancestry of man, one of his former students, a young Dutch doctor named Eugene Dubois, went forth with the avowed intention of finding the "missing link." At the time this seemed like the most hare-brained thing in the world to do, since he had to give up a promising career as a teacher of anatomy at Amsterdam, and since there was virtually no shred of evidence in support of his scheme. Nevertheless, fortune smiled on Dubois and, by a piece of impossibly good luck, he did indeed find what he was looking for. As an indication of the improbability of his venture, in the only other instance where an expedition set out with the deliberate intent of finding early man, the reward was the discovery of dinosaur eggs.

Plagued by a lack of funds—his project sounded so absurd that no one was willing to back him—Dubois signed up as a health officer in the Dutch colonial forces in what is now Indonesia. He was first assigned to Sumatra, where he spent several years hunting fossils. A variety of circumstances led him to suspect that Java was a more likely area, and in 1889 he got himself transferred there. He remained in Java for the next five years, and there made the discoveries for which he will always be remembered. In 1890 he discovered a small fragment of a lower jaw whose importance was only recognized later. In 1891 his excavations unearthed a skullcap with such a low forehead and heavy brow ridge, and with such marked constriction between the brow and the brain case, that he attributed it to a chimpanzee. In 1892, some 50 feet away from the skull in the same layer, he found a thighbone (femur) which was practically indistinguishable from the femur of modern man. This he claimed belonged to the individual represented by the skull, and for a while believed that he had discovered an erect walking chimpanzee. Comparative studies and measurements forced him to alter his opinion, since the skull, however primitive or apelike in form, was half way between that of man and that of chimpanzee in gross size, possessing a brain which fell within the lower limits of the normal modern range of variation. This he realized was his missing link, but (in contrast to the semi-erect posture which had been attributed to the Spy and Neanderthal finds) it was an erect walking missing link. So he slightly modified Haeckel's designation and, in his monograph of 1894, christened his discovery *Pithecanthropus erectus*. This still serves as the type specimen for our Pithecanthropine stage, although it is no longer regarded as a separate genus.

Dubois' admirable monograph created an international sensation and, when he returned to Europe in 1895, he was an immediate celebrity. The International Zoological Congress met at Leyden in 1895, where Dubois and his Pithecanthropus were the focus of attention of an unparalleled gathering of famous scholars. After prolonged argument, three schools of thought emerged. One, siding with Dubois, felt that Pithecanthropus was neither ape nor man, but a genuine transitional form. Another felt that it was on the human side of the boundary—primitive, perhaps, but really man. The third group, headed by the aged Virchow, regarded it as being a giant form of gibbon, interesting and unusual but only an ape after all. The controversy continued unresolved for many years without conclusion, and it was not until the late 1920's and 1930's, when more Pithecanthropine skeletal remains were discovered in China near Peking, and also in Java, that general acceptance was possible. The Chinese Pithecanthropines, originally christened *Sinanthropus pekinensis* in 1927, were associated with stone tools and ancient hearths, which confirmed the implications of the human status of the Pithecanthropines as a whole. Paradoxically, among the very few voices now raised in opposition to the human status of Pithecanthropus was that of the elderly Dubois himself. Although he was willing to accept the new discoveries of Java and China as genuine early men, he reverted to, and for the last 20 years of his life professed, the opinion voiced by Virchow in 1895 (that his original Pithecanthropus was actually a giant gibbon) and would not accept the new Java and China men as Pithecanthropines—as descendants of what he now considered were not even transitional ape-men, but apes.

While full confirmation for the significance of Pithecanthropus had to wait some 30 years, most scholars at and following the turn of the century came to feel that it could be regarded as an extremely primitive form of man. What with Pithecanthropus, Neanderthal, and modern forms of man established at different times, and at least the latter two associated with different archaeological traditions, it was possible, during the first years of the twentieth century, to suggest a logical evolutionary scheme containing all the known human fossils arranged in terms of relationships and chronology. This was done by Gustav Schwalbe, professor of anatomy at the University of Strassburg, who capped a series of papers and monographs of the late nineteenth and early twentieth centuries with his summary work, *Studies on the Prehistory of Man*, published in 1906. In this he tentatively proposed a picture of the evolutionary history of man comprising three successive stages—Pithecanthropus, Neanderthal, and Mod-

Gustav Schwalbe (1844–1916), Strassburg anatomist and physical anthropologist, who first arranged the known human fossils in an evolutionary sequence. (Courtesy Ashley Montagu.)

ern—allowing for the possibility of adjustments and modifications which future finds would make inevitable.

Schwalbe's scheme was useful, flexible, and in accord with the evidence available at that time. With one major addition, it proved valuable enough to provide the organizing principle behind the interpretations offered in the later chapters of this book, although, for reasons which will be considered in the pages that follow, it has been generally rejected and forgotten by the anthropological world.

Four   Hominid   Catastrophism

In 1907, the year following Schwalbe's summary, a brief wave of excitement surrounded the discovery of an enormous mandible in a gravel pit near the village of Mauer, not far from the city of Heidelberg in western Germany. Without the rest of the skull, interpretations were somewhat inhibited, although the primitive characteristics were obvious. Still, the stratigraphy was precisely documented, indicating that the Heidelberg jaw was, as it remains, by far the oldest human fossil discovered in western Europe, possibly a contemporary or even a representative of the Pithecanthropines of the Far East.

In 1908, however, the scene of discovery shifted and the tide of historical accident began which is so largely responsible for the present interpretations of human evolution in general and of the Neanderthals in particular. At Le Moustier in southwestern France—the same village which gave its name to the tool-making tradition associated with the Neanderthals—a genuine Neanderthal burial was discovered. For a variety of reasons (initially related to the somewhat dubious activities of the discoverer, a Swiss antiquities dealer who had been looting French archaeological sites and selling the booty to the highest bidder), the description was delayed for many years, and as a result the Le Moustier skeleton never played the role it deserved. It finally met oblivion by a World War II bomb, and its full significance will never be known.

To make up for this, later in the same year and not far from the same region in southwestern France, another and more complete Neanderthal skeleton was discovered in excavations near the village of La Chapelle-aux-Saints. These remains were entrusted to Marcellin Boule, paleontologist at the National Museum of Natural History in Paris. During the next five years he produced a series of scholarly papers, climaxed by a massive monograph in three installments, appearing in 1911, 1912, and 1913. Boule's portrayal of this, the most complete Neanderthal skeleton yet discovered, formed the basis for the caricature of the cave man espoused by an entire subsequent generation of cartoonists, journalists, and, alas, professional scholars. The "Old Man" of La Chapelle-aux-Saints was depicted as being a creature structurally intermediate between modern man and the anthropoid apes.

The great toe was presumed to diverge, hinting that it still preserved a degree of opposability to the other toes, and, in doing so, it forced the possessors to walk on the outer margins of the feet in the awkward manner of the modern orang. Details of the knee joint were taken to indicate that it could not be entirely extended, meaning that the Neanderthals were not completely erect and could do no better than to shuffle along with a "bent-knee gait." This also was supposed to indicate their similarity to modern apes, although since apes are perfectly capable of fully extending their legs, such claims demonstrate an ignorance of the anatomy and functioning of the knee joint in both apes and men. The same issues had been raised concerning the Spy skeletons, and several detailed studies before the end of the nineteenth century demonstrated how inapplicable they were, but Boule chose to ignore these. In harmony with the semi-erect picture conjured up by his discussion of the feet and legs, Boule claimed that the reverse curves present in the human neck and lower back were absent, as in the modern apes, and that the whole trunk indicated a powerful but incompletely upright postural adaptation. On top of this scarcely human caricature was a head which hung forward instead of being balanced on top of the spinal column. A detailed study of a cast made of the interior of the braincase convinced him that the brain was inferior in organization to that of modern man, particularly in the frontal lobes which, ever since the days when phrenology was respectable, everyone knows are related to the higher functionings of the mind.

The continued and repeated use of words such as "ape-like," "primitive," and "inferior" was not lost on the fascinated public, which quickly invested the Neanderthals with a veritable hairy pelt and long simian arms, although there is no evidence whatever concerning hair and the arms were actually relatively short. In the years since that time, it has been demonstrated that Boule was in error on each one of the foregoing points, but the vision of the totality has not been altered and the Neanderthals continue to shuffle through the pages of numberless books and slouch stupidly in countless cartoons.

Having produced this caricature, Boule then proclaimed that it could have nothing to do with the ancestors of modern man. As justification, he claimed that the Neanderthals and their culture came to an abrupt end and were suddenly replaced by full *Homo sapiens*, sweeping into Europe with their superior Upper Palaeolithic technology. Furthermore, said he, men of modern form already existed during the time when the Neanderthals were the main occupants of the European scene. This latter claim has provided one of the main stimuli for subsequent activities in human paleontology, since within a year Boule's candidate for this ancient modern was disqualified. From that time on, an entire generation of anthropologists has been searching for the as-yet-undiscovered *sapiens* in the Middle Pleistocene or even earlier.

Within the same year that the final installment of Boule's ponderous work appeared, an ingenious Englishman had fabricated the famous Piltdown fraud which confused the picture for a full 40 years before being exposed. Piltdown turned out to be fragments of the cranium of a modern man and part of the jaw of a modern female orang, stained to look ancient, appropriately broken and artificially worn, and mingled with a collection of extinct animal bones acquired from all over the world before being scattered in a gravel pocket in southeastern England. Also in the same year Gustav Schwalbe published a review of Boule's monograph which, at 80 pages, was nearly a book in itself. In this he yielded to the picture painted by Boule and abandoned his own former claims that the Neanderthals were the direct ancestors of modern man, although he noted the evidence contradicting Boule's claim of ancient moderns. Schwalbe never abandoned Pithecanthropus, which he continued to regard as ancestral to all later forms of man, although Boule had indicated that he considered *both* Neanderthal and Pithecanthropus to be branches off to the side of the main stream of human evolution, branches which became extinct without issue.

In 1914, the year after Boule's publication, the First World War burst upon Europe. The dislocation of human affairs and the cessation of scholarly activity are inevitable companions of war, but in the field which pursues the study of human evolution, the legacy of this conflict has been

Aleš Hrdlička (1869–1943). Born in Czechoslovakia, raised in the United States, he was the first physical anthropologist at the Smithsonian Institution and one of the most distinguished representatives of the field in America. Hrdlička was one of the very few scholars after the first World War who continued to view the Neanderthals as a stage in human evolution [See his The Skeletal Remains of Early Man, 1930]. (Courtesy of the Smithsonian Institution.)

more enduring if less clearly appreciated. Germany not only lost the war, but suffered a blow to her intellectual prestige which has had repercussions ever since. In the post-war era, Germany's intellectual recovery was progressively stifled by the rise of the Hitler regime which, when it came to power, quickly extinguished what had managed to survive. This was particularly true for any science which attempted to make an objective and unbiased study of human beings. Anthropology and the other social sciences suffered severely and have seen few contributions made and have played but a minor role in the general advances made in other countries. Little remains of the pre-World War I tradition in German anthropology and, while I can hear my colleagues muttering that this is really a good thing, yet the valuable parts have been eliminated along with the bad ones. It is to be regretted for instance that so little is remembered of the pre-Boule writings of Gustav Schwalbe.

Before proceeding, it should be interesting to consider briefly the source of Boule's orientation. Boule was a paleontologist, trained during the 80's of the previous century in an academic environment which had not accepted the Darwinian view of evolution. Although French paleontologists spoke of "evolution," they carefully distinguished it from "darwinism." To them, evolution signified the appearance of successive organic forms, whereas "darwinism" meant the development of later forms out of earlier ones by natural processes, and this they refused to accept. When questioned concerning the source of the successive forms, they would evoke

24

extinctions followed by invasions from elsewhere, and, ultimately, successive creations. This, then, was simply the survival of Cuvier's "catastrophism," re-labeled "evolution," and this was what Marcellin Boule applied to the human fossil record. As he noted, modern forms of men appeared more recently than Neanderthals, so, following the tradition in which he was trained, he postulated Neanderthal extinction and subsequent modern invasion. This of course presupposed the existence of modern forms elsewhere, about which he, like Cuvier a century before, was relatively vague, and which has caused his followers a considerable degree of mental anguish ever since.

This view can be labeled **hominid catastrophism**, and, because of the historical accidents of the second decade of the present century, it has continued to dominate interpretations of human evolution, although it appears in a variety of forms and has been substantially modified. Following the First World War, Boule treated the totality of the known human fossil record, presenting his scheme of hominid catastrophism—labeled "evolution"—in a single volume, *Fossil Men*. This book has continued to influence the field; an edition revised after Boule's death by a former student still remains as one of the few summary treatments.

Five Between
World Wars

During the course of the years, far more fossils have been discovered than there is room even to begin to record in a treatment as brief as this. Some of these, relatively important specimens, must be omitted because they have not met the criterion of contributing substantially to alterations in the over-all picture. The next discovery which did measure up was made in 1924; although it was but a little fossil for which only modest claims were made, in retrospect it can be regarded as a major portent of what was to come.

The scene was South Africa, where a small fossil skull was given to Raymond Dart, the young professor of anatomy at the medical school of the University of Witwatersrand in Johannesburg. Dart had recently finished his training in medicine, anatomy, and physical anthropology in London, and was keenly aware that Africa, cited by Darwin as the possible source for the human line of development, had up to that time yielded no dated early human material at all. Only the single enigmatic and undated find of a Neanderthal-like skull in a mine shaft in Northern Rhodesia existed to demonstrate the presence of an earlier stage in human evolution. The little skull handed to Dart was that of an immature individual—approximately at the same stage of development as that of a modern six-year-old child—and it is a risky business to establish taxonomic affinity or evolutionary stage on the basis of specimens in which growth has not been completed. Still, Dart's study, published early in 1925, was able to demonstrate that this juvenile creature had a brain the size of a large adult gorilla, that its head was balanced atop the spinal column instead of slung forward, that the palate was human rather than ape-like in shape, and that, despite the great size of the teeth, the canines did not project beyond the level of the other teeth. Although he correctly noted that juvenile apes are less distinct from juvenile humans in some of these features than is the case where comparisons are made between adults of various forms, yet he could state in summary that this South African fossil, blasted out of a quarry at Taung, presented a curious mixture of ape-like and human features. Withal he regarded it as an extinct ape—closer perhaps to the human line than any yet discovered, but an ape nevertheless—and christened it *Australopithecus africanus* (Southern ape of Africa).

Dart's sober and relatively cautious appraisal was greated by an outburst of patronizing scorn from the evolutionary and anatomical authorities back in England, several of whom were his former teachers. Chief among

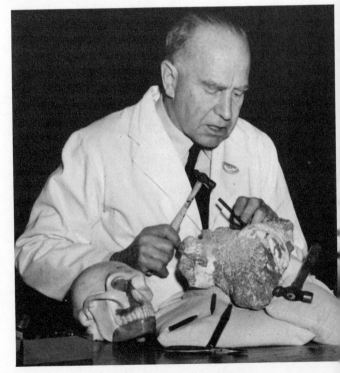

Raymond A. Dart, whose prophetic interpretation of Australopithecus went unappreciated for more than thirty years. (Photo courtesy of Professor Raymond Dart.)

The first Australopithecine to be discovered, Dart's original Australopithecus africanus. (Courtesy of the American Museum of Natural History.)

these was Sir Arthur Keith, champion of the Piltdown fraud, who repeatedly stated that Dart's position was "preposterous." In fairness it should be pointed out that Keith was in no way to be blamed for the fraudulent facets of the Piltdown melange, since he was as badly—even tragically—misled by it as anyone. Yet of all the criticism offered of Dart's views, only a relatively trivial one remains, and this concerns the fact that he mixed terms of Latin and Greek origin in assigning the fossil its name.

There seem to have been two sources for the reaction to Dart's claims. One was the feeling that the fossil should really have been turned over to the "proper authorities" (those back in England) for study. The second was based on the feeling that, with Pithecanthropus finally accepted as the earliest possible form of man, anything demonstrably more primitive, as Australopithecus was, even had it grown to adulthood, could not conceivably belong in the picture. Influenced by such considerations, "Dart's child," as Australopithecus was deprecatingly referred to, was relegated to the category of "just another fossil ape."

The excitement over Australopithecus was soon superseded by the discovery of Pithecanthropines in China, the so-called **Sinanthropus** remains or Pekin man. During the succeeding decade, fragments of more than 40 individuals were retrieved from the limestone caves of Choukoutien, only a few miles southwest of Pekin (now Peiping). Ultimately these were the subject of a series of masterly monographs by Franz Weidenreich, a refugee from Hitler's Germany and, by great good fortune, one of the very few who perpetuated the thinking of his late teacher and colleague, Gustav Schwalbe. War, with its inevitable disrupting influence, spelled final oblivion for the original Sinanthropus material, which was last seen

Franz Weidenreich (1873–1948) shown with Dr. G. H. R. von Koenigswald. (Courtesy of the American Museum of Natural History.)

on December 7, 1941, when the outbreak of war in the Pacific caught them at Chin Wang Tao, the port of embarkation, on the verge of being shipped to the United States for safekeeping. No trace of them has since been found, but, during their brief resurrection, excellent casts were made and they were drawn, photographed, and exhaustively described in Weidenreich's splendid publications. If any doubt had remained concerning the human status of the Pithecanthropines, it was now dispelled.

The 1930's also saw important discoveries in other parts of the world. A skull from Steinheim in Germany (1933) and the back of a skull from Swanscombe in England (1935 and 1936) partially serve to fill the long gap between the time of the Pithecanthropines and that of the Neanderthals, although their interpretation is still the subject of prolonged debate. More important, however, were discoveries made in the Middle East and again in South Africa. The Middle Eastern finds were the result of excavations on the slopes of Mount Carmel, in Palestine, little more than a mile from the shores of the Mediterranean. There, in the years 1931 and 1932, a joint Anglo-American archaeological expedition discovered the remains of at least a dozen fossil humans in two different caves. The one complete skeleton from the cave of Tabūn was of a female which was in other respects indistinguishable from the classic Neanderthals of Europe. This at least demonstrated that the Neanderthals were not a limited Euro-

30

pean phenomenon. This point was also demonstrated by the simultaneous discovery of a series of skulls, approaching Pithecanthropine form but still within the Neanderthal spectrum, in Java, only 20 miles downstream from Trinil, where the original Pithecanthropus had been found. Recently, more full Neanderthals have been found at Shanidar cave in northern Iraq, again attesting to Neanderthal distribution.

The second Palestinian cave, Mugharet es-Skhūl, divulged the remains of at least 10 individuals, but rather than exhibiting fully Neanderthal form, they displayed characteristics which were half way between Neanderthal and Modern. This has earned them the designation of "Neanderthaloid"—that is, recalling the Neanderthals on the one hand, but not to a sufficient degree to separate them from modern man on the other. By one of those little ironies which only fate can arrange, the major burden of description and interpretation fell to Sir Arthur Keith. He who had been so critical of Dart's attempt to make sense out of a mixture of simian and human traits was now confronted with the task of interpreting a mixture of Neanderthal and modern ones, and his vacillations between alternate possibilities satisfied no one. Opinion tended to regard both Mount Carmel

Sir Arthur Keith (1866–1955), best known and most influential of British physical anthropologists. (Brown Brothers.)

sites as third interglacial, i.e. before the fourth and last Pleistocene ice advance and therefore before the time of the European Neanderthals. Such being the case, Tabūn was reasonable enough, but Skhūl remained a dilemma. Keith faced the problem squarely but could not decide whether Skhūl indicated the hybridization of a fully Neanderthal population (represented by Tabūn) and the long-sought but as-yet-undiscovered modern one, or whether it was a Neanderthal population in the throes of rapid evolutionary change in the direction of modern man. He seemed to favor the latter explanation, although others have stressed the former. In any case, the issue has been drastically changed by recent refinements in dating, which have removed both Mount Carmel sites from the third interglacial. It now appears that Tabūn is little more than 40,000 years old, contemporary with the very latest full Neanderthals, and Skhūl is some 5,000 years more recent, being half way between the latest Neanderthal and the oldest Modern.

Because of the dating difficulties, the Mount Carmel problem remained unsolved for a full 30 years. Meanwhile, in 1936, old issues of another sort were re-opened, and this time the evidence was sufficient enough to ward off attempts to sweep them under the rug. Just when it seemed that the furor over Dart's Australopithecus had been reduced to a memory, another fortunate explosion occurred. This particular blast took place in a lime works quarry at Sterkfontein, some miles west of Johannesburg in the

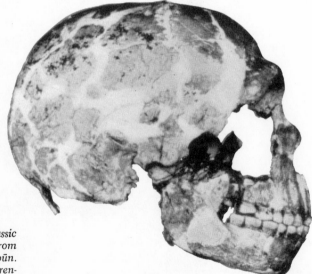

The skull of a classic Neanderthal woman from the cave of et-Tabūn. (Courtesy of the Clarendon Press, Oxford.)

Transvaal area of South Africa. Fossil bones were discovered as a result and, by good fortune, were delivered into the hands of the venerable vertebrate paleontologist Robert Broom. Fragments of nearly half a dozen creatures were included, among them a complete adult skull. Broom immediately recognized the similarity of these to Australopithecus—eventually he advocated an entire taxonomic subfamily, the Australopithecinae, to include them all—but he believed that the new finds were different enough to warrant new generic and specific designations. He called them *Plesianthropus transvaalensis*. Time has shown that they are simply adult versions of Australopithecus, and so, for the present at least, they will simply be referred to as the early Australopithecines.

The upright carriage of the head and the extraordinarily human appearance of the distal end of a femur contributed to the suspicion that these creatures may have been erect walking bipeds, and it began to appear as though Dart had not been so rash as his detractors had claimed. Nor was this all. Two years later, in 1938, on a farm named Kromdraai some two miles from Sterkfontein, more Australopithecine remains were discovered and brought to the attention of Robert Broom. Fragments of skull, jaws, teeth, arm, hand, and foot bones suggested a similar but a larger creature, which Broom called *Paranthropus robustus* and which we shall refer to *en masse* as the later Australopithecines.

Now, with the weight of Broom's years of paleontological experience and the quantity of accumulating evidence, the Australopithecines could no longer be passed off as figments of a youthful fancy. However, consistent with the principles of hominid catastrophism, modified or extreme, and convinced that men of modern form would yet be discovered in the early Pleistocene, most anthropologists supported the view that the Australopithecines were simply another side branch from the main stem of human evolution and had become extinct without issue. To be sure, a few anthropologists, notably the American student of the Neanderthals, Hrdlička, and Franz Weidenreich, complained that the human evolutionary tree portrayed by most scholars was in effect all branches and no trunk, but real qualms did not develop until after the Second World War.

With the close of the 1930's war came to the West and, as invariably happens under such circumstances, fossil hunting ceased and evolutionary studies were seriously impeded. Fortunately, the conflagration was delayed a while in the Far East, and work continued for a time in China and Java. The last major find of the pre-war era in the East was made by the Dutch paleontologist, G. H. R. von Koenigswald, who had been responsible for further Pithecanthropine finds in Java throughout the late 1930's. Just before the Japanese occupation in 1941, he found a small fragment of an enormous mandible. The teeth were clearly human in form, but immense, and he gave it the relatively jaw-breaking name, *Meganthropus palaeo-javanicus*. A similar mandible, found in the same area in 1952, confirmed the genuineness of the first find, and comparative study has revealed a fact of great consequence: *Meganthropus palaeojavanicus* is not significantly different from Broom's *Paranthropus* in dating, size, or form!

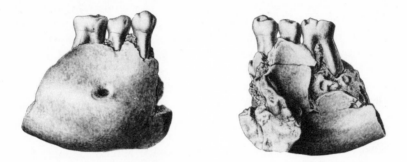

Meganthropus palaeojavanicus, *a Paranthropus type of Australopithecine from Java. (Courtesy of Dr. G. H. R. von Koenigswald.)*

Dr. Robert Broom (1866–1951), *physician and paleontologist, with a cast of Pleisianthropus. (Courtesy of the American Museum of Natural History.)*

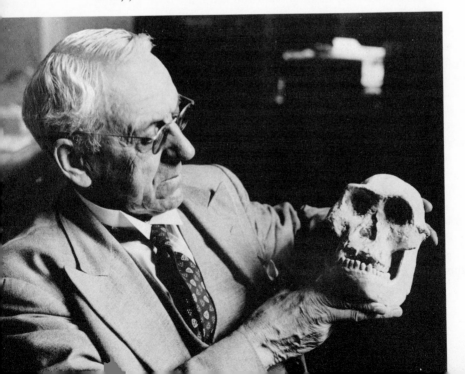

Six Recent
Discoveries

In 1947, soon after peace made it possible once again to return to his prehistoric research, Dr. Broom, now more than 80 years of age but undiminished in energy, resumed his investigations of Sterkfontein. Within a short time he discovered quantities of Australopithecine remains, among which was a nearly complete half pelvis. This bone was remarkably like the pelvis of modern man and, of all the Australopithecine fragments found to date, most clearly demonstrated their erect and bipedal mode of locomotion. Yet traditional anthropological doubts were raised, and it was hinted by some that perhaps the pelvic fragment properly belonged to the long-sought true man and had nothing to do with Australopithecines. Variants of this argument continue to be offered concerning other fragments of evidence but, like the cry of "pathological" which was repeatedly applied to early human fossils in the late nineteenth century, this has begun to sound more than a little strained.

The year 1947 also saw the return of Raymond Dart to the arena of Australopithecine research. His work was concentrated on a deserted limeworks dump at Makapansgat, some 200 miles northeast of Sterkfontein. This dump produced a wealth of Australopithecine fragments, evidently of the same sort as those of Taung and Sterkfontein, although Dart gave them a new specific name. Within two years Dart had also recovered substantial fragments of pelvis which, if anything, were even more man-like than those from Sterkfontein. In 1947 also, Sir Arthur Keith published a handsome and gracious apology, noting that it was he who had been rash and hasty in 1925 and that time and events had proven Dart's interpretation to be much more nearly correct than his own.

Starting in the succeeding year, 1948, Broom and his assistant, J. T. Robinson, began work at another site, Swartkrans, a short distance from Sterkfontein, where they soon found Australopithecines of the same sort that Broom had found at Kromdraai 10 years before. Adding still another dimension to the early Pleistocene fossil picture as seen in the Transvaal of South Africa, a pocket in the Swartkrans site produced another form of human fossil. The first fragment, a nearly complete jaw found in 1949, was initially given the name of *Telanthropus capensis*, but comparative study has recently convinced Robinson that it is not distinguishable from the Pithecanthropines of Asia. As such, it is a find of the greatest significance. Dart and his assistants at Makapansgat and, following Broom's death in 1951, Robinson at Swartkrans and Sterkfontein, continued to recover fossil fragments of various kinds during the succeeding decade.

With the confusing welter of names, dates, sites, and fragmentary fossils emanating from South Africa, some simplification is in order. Evidently two forms of Australopithecine and a Pithecanthropine are represented. Australopithecus, the smaller and earlier form, has been identified at Taung, Sterkfontein, and Makapansgat. Paranthropus, the later and larger form, has been found at Kromdraai and Swartkrans. The Pithecanthropine also comes from Swartkrans, although there is no assurance that the pocket which contains it is the same age as the Paranthropus part. In fact, the whole problem of the dating and associations of the South African sites is still very far from solution. Adding to the confusion is the fact that early stone tools are present in South Africa and have even been found in the later layers of Sterkfontein. Discussion of the implications of these facts shall, however, be deferred to a later chapter.

The two decades since the end of the Second World War have seen the discovery of human fossil material from all corners of the world, representing all stages of human evolution. Some, such as the extensive Neanderthal discoveries at Shanidar cave in northern Iraq (starting in 1953), are of major significance, but so far the finds from sub-Saharan Africa have not yielded the center of the stage. The scope of this book does not allow me to indulge in the treatment of more than a fraction of these fascinating finds, although I must confess that my enthusiasm is in no way reduced by finding myself confined to the discoveries of greatest dramatic import.

The final facet of this historical review will be concerned with the discoveries of Dr. and Mrs. L. S. B. Leakey at Olduvai Gorge, Tanganyika (now Tanzania), in East Africa. While the finds which made them famous did not begin to occur until 1959, the basis which makes these discoveries so important goes back more than a third of a century, to when Dr. Leakey first started making expeditions to this area. His general experience in East African prehistory goes back even further, but he first visited Olduvai Gorge in 1931 and shortly discovered tools of a type as crude as or cruder than those of any known tradition. Because of their location, these have been called Oldowan tools; they are now regarded as constituting the oldest tool-making tradition in the world. The Leakeys' continued work in Olduvai Gorge has revealed the development of the Oldowan tradition through the ascending layers until it becomes the familiar "hand-axe" tradition recognized a century ago by Boucher de Perthes at Abbeville and widely distributed throughout the Middle Pleistocene of the Old World. Here, then, is the Lower Pleistocene parent of the hand-axe and, by extension, the Lower Pleistocene parent of all subsequent human cultural traditions including our own—a confirmation of Darwin's prediction made so long ago!

As if this were not enough of a contribution to have made during a lifetime, the Leakeys' continued persistence in the face of formidable financial and environmental obstacles has finally rewarded them with the discovery of the manufacturer of the Oldowan tools—the bones of what must be our own ancestors. On July 17, 1959, they discovered their first fossil "man." Although they followed the confusing paleontological practice of giving it a new generic and specific name, *Zinjanthropus boisei*, it turns out to be nothing less than an Australopithecine—one of the later, or Paranthropus, variety—in spite of a number of relatively minor features cited as being distinctive.

The discovery of an Australopithecine in the midst of a living floor where Oldowan tools were in the course of being manufactured should have removed all doubts concerning the identity of the most remote human ancestors. But still the search for ancient moderns goes on; for it has been suggested that perhaps it was some as-yet-undiscovered "true man" who was the Oldowan tool-maker and who had lunched upon the Leakeys' Australopithecine. Among the proponents of this view are the Leakeys themselves and, while this is obviously at variance with the interpretation favored here, it should be noted that one of the goads which has driven them on over so many years of often thankless toil has been the desire to find this ancient phantom.

Bolstered by the flood of acclaim and support which followed their 1959 discovery, the Leakeys returned to the hard work of finding more fossil men. Late in 1960 they discovered fragments of jaw, leg, and foot of even greater age than their Zinjanthropus. Of still more importance, they found a skullcap from an early Middle Pleistocene level associated with an Abbevillian type of tool-making tradition; from all appearances, it can be regarded as an African version of the Pithecanthropines.

In 1962, 1963, and 1964, continued work at Olduvai produced the remains of five additional fossil hominids from above the level of Bed I, and one extremely important mandible from the shores of Lake Natron, some 50 miles northeast of Olduvai. Most of these finds were made in Bed II in 1963, and Dr. Leakey has christened them with yet another name, *Homo habilis*, suggesting that they are of the same form as the Pre-Zinj fragments. He believes that this is his long-sought "true man," contemporary with his Zinj-type Australopithecine, and the maker of the tools. The data offered in support of this are quite insufficient to warrant such a theoretically unlikely view, and one suspects that when analysis has been completed and/or more material is available, the new Bed II hominids will prove to be African Pithecanthropines, as was the Bed II skull of 1960. The Lake Natron mandible, however, is a clear counterpart to the Zinj skull, and is further evidence for the presence of one of the later and larger Australopithecines in East Africa, although the age correspondence with the Olduvai strata is still a problem. Not only, then, has Olduvai

The "Zinjanthropus" skull from Olduvai Gorge, a Paranthropus type mandible from Peninj near Lake Natron. (Photo by: R. I. M. Campbell, Nairobi, Kenya.)

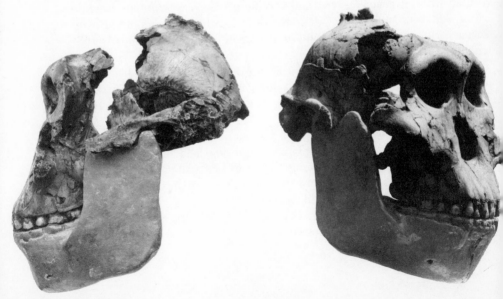

Olduvai Gorge, Tanzania. (Courtesy George H. Hansen.)

Gorge revealed the first crucial stages in the development of human stone tool-making traditions, but it has shown that these are associated with human fossils of known form in a sequence which logically fits the morphological progression. Equally important is the fact that geological conditions have proved to be ideal for the use of Potassium-Argon dating techniques, the one form of radioactive age determination which works for early Pleistocene strata. By these means, their Pithecanthropines are 500,000 years old, and their Australopithecines are 1.75 million years old, and more.

For sequence, perspective, and significance, there is no single locality in the world which can come close to Olduvai Gorge. Even as this is being written, the Leakeys are at work in the effort to discover more and still older skeletal remains. As the earth continues to divulge its secrets, it seems more than likely that Olduvai Gorge will come to be regarded as the standard of reference, an earthy encyclopedia used for the comparison of all early human material of both an archaeological and a skeletal nature— in fact, a veritable yardstick for human evolution.

Seven Evolutionary Principles

Many approaches to the subject of human evolution are restricted to descriptions of the fossil evidence, or perhaps to the events surrounding the discovery of the major fragments. However fascinating these may be (here I suspect my own enthusiasm for the bony details of long defunct hominids may somewhat outrun that of the beginning student or general reader), they do not automatically ensure the full understanding of what is being described. Somewhere along the line, one should encounter a resume of the major principles of evolution in general, and the forces which act on man in particular. Finally, these should be specifically applied to the human fossil record, and the role which they have played in the production of the specific changes noted should be delineated. This last will be the subject of the final chapters; meanwhile, a brief consideration will be given to the major evolutionary principles which are important to consider in human evolution.

Natural Selection

The first and most important of the evolutionary principles is encompassed by the term **natural selection**. Like many other basic principles in other areas of thought (culture for the anthropologist, or entropy for the physicist, for example), it is hard to define concisely, although natural scientists are virtually unanimous in its usage. Realizing that this is an oversimplification, one can regard natural selection as being **the sum total of naturally occurring forces which influence the relative chances for survival and perpetuation of the various manifestations of organic life.**

Credit can be given to Charles Darwin for using this as the major explanatory principle necessary to account for the cumulative change apparent in the history of any given organic line. Occasionally the principle has been tersely expressed as "survival of the fittest," although Darwin himself never stated it in these terms, and indeed they have been justly criticized as being not quite accurate. In the recent past it has been pointed out that evolutionary survival is determined more by reproductive success than by physical strength. The suggestion has been made that the phrase might be modified to read "the survival of the fit." Actually, there is a certain amount of verbal quibbling which must inevitably surround any attempt to produce a precise definition since, if fitness is described in terms of the production of viable offspring, then the fittest will obviously be those who produce the most and whose traits will be most frequently represented in subsequent generations.

As environmental forces change over time, the characteristics which have greatest survival value will not be those which were most valuable at an earlier age. However, in order that environmental forces may effect a change in the characteristic appearance of the species in question—i.e. in order for natural selection to produce evolution—some source for the new traits must be postulated. In Darwin's day this source was unknown. On the basis of extensive observational experience, however, he knew that the variants were always being produced—so he simply accepted their existence "on faith," without knowing where they came from. Some of the most bitter attacks against him came from those who recognized that he did take it that way.

Today we recognize that the faith Darwin had in his observation that variation occurs in the normal course of events was faith well grounded. When developments in the field of genetics led to the recognition of mutations as the sources of variation, it was soon explicitly realized that "mutations provide the raw materials for natural selection." As has been mentioned, this was the point where evolutionary thought and genetics joined to produce what has come to be called **the synthetic theory of evolution.**

The Probable Mutation Effect

If the summed forces of nature working on organic variability can be regarded as the most important principle in the production of evolutionary change, then the next most important dimension must be that which is determined by the nature and frequency of the sources of variation themselves. Simply stated, **the nature of mutations, their frequency of occurrence, and the probable effect which they have are of an importance second only to natural selection.**

Although a discussion of genetics at the molecular level may seem rather a long way from the human fossil record, its importance will become quite clear during the discussion of all but one of the major changes which characterize the course of human evolution. In essence, the story goes like this: During the last decade, research has identified the basic genetic material, postulated its structure, and suggested the mode of action whereby it controls organic form and function, as well as replicates itself. To say that the basic genetic material is DNA is true enough, but to say that a mutation is an error in the attempt by a DNA molecule to copy itself, while true, is not precise enough for our purposes. To appreciate the significance of the average mutation, one must first have some idea of how genetic control normally works.

For the moment we are concerned with two kinds of organic molecules: nucleic acids and proteins. Both are **polymers**—that is, they are chain-like structures whose links are called **amino acids** in the case of proteins and **nucleotides** in the case of nucleic acids. The full nucleic acid molecule is a double chain composed of identical halves; each being the complement or mirror image of the other. However, whereas the double chain of a nucleic acid is built up of only four different kinds of nucleotides in all possible combinations, there are more than 20 kinds of amino acids available for the construction of a protein.

Both kinds of molecules are of vital importance. Proteins not only form the structural building-blocks of which living organisms are constructed (bone, muscle, fiber), but they also constitute the organic catalysts called **enzymes** (adrenalin, insulin, hemoglobin), without which normal metabolic functioning and growth could not occur. DNA, on the other hand, remains within the nucleus of the cell, where it provides a source of information for the construction of protein molecules.

At first it was not known how the four nucleotides of nucleic acids related to the 20-plus amino acids of proteins. To simplify the rather complex process that subsequent research has shown is involved, let us put it this way: various sequences of nucleotides, taken three at a time, can specify (serve as a code for) given amino acids. The nucleotides, with the aid of specific enzymes, fasten together the amino acids by means of a phosphate energy bond. In the course of protein production, quantities of nucleotide triplets attach themselves to free amino acids and tow them to the sites of protein synthesis within the cell, where they are lined up and snapped together.

This brief and actually grossly oversimplified description is not intended to be complete. The point to be made is that a sequence of three specific nucleotides identifies one particular amino acid. If by chance an error is made in the replication of the nucleic acid molecule, the smallest identifiable change will be the modification of a single nucleotide. Although a single nucleotide does not correspond to an entire amino acid, the modification of any one nucleotide will indeed change the nature of the triplet to which it belongs, and in all likelihood this in turn will code a different amino acid from the previous one—if indeed it codes any.

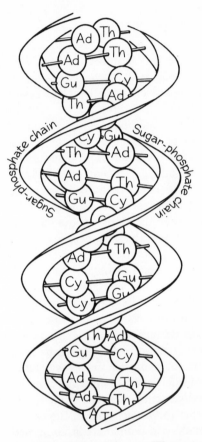

The double helix, or Watson-Crick, model of a DNA molecule.

Two of the most likely changes at the single nucleotide level result in still further complications. The addition or deletion of a nucleotide will not only modify the triplet within which it occurs, but will also change

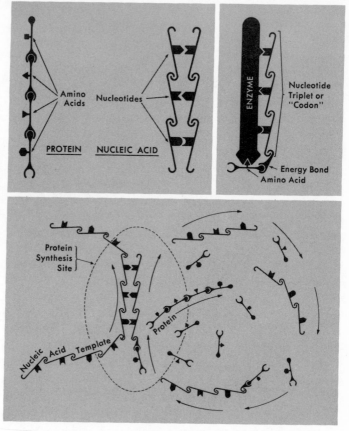

Left, schematic representation of a protein molecule, made up of amino acid units in a chain; and of a nucleic acid molecule, made up of nucleotide units in a chain. Right, attachment of a specific amino acid to a particular nucleotide triplet with the aid of an enzyme specially constructed for that purpose. Bottom, amino acids being towed by nucleotide triplets to the site where they are hooked together to form proteins.

the nature of the triplets that follow. Obviously, this means more than one amino acid in the related protein will be changed, and it seems quite clear that the protein will not work in the way it was intended. A change in even one amino acid can drastically alter the function of the protein of which it is a part, as can be seen in sickle cell anemia and a variety of other deficiency diseases of an inherited nature.

What we have been discussing forms the basis for the fact realized nearly 40 years ago that the great majority of mutations will be disadvantageous to the organism in which they occur. Actually this statement, while correct, assumes a static picture in which environmental forces remain unchanged—that is, it assumes that any modification in an organism will be detrimental to it. To be sure, when an organism is well adapted to its environment, most alterations in its form which arise by chance will not be advantageous, but there is always the case to be considered where the environment itself undergoes a change, in which instance there may be some structures which will be less important for the organism's

47

survival. While this is not a major problem in evolution, it is one which continually arises, and, since it has apparently occurred in the course of human development, it deserves some attention.

When some major change occurs in a creature's environment, or it enters an entirely new one, it may suddenly find that it possesses some structures which, while not disadvantageous, are of no particular value to it. Since the structures in question are neither selected for nor selected against, they are at the mercy of random variation. It is now pertinent to ask what sort of variations are likely to occur. If we are dealing with a feature of gross morphology (teeth, horns, pigmentation), we must realize that these are the products of a period of growth during which development

Normal ....the ten hen net

Mutated by   ⌐(h)
  deletion of H ......tet enh enn et

or,   (t)
  addition of T.......tth ete nhe nne t

or,   (n)⟍ ⌐(h)
  substitution
  of N for H.........the ten hen net

The effects of deletion, addition, and substitution on the "sense" of a phrase made up of three-letter words (triplets) composed of only four kinds of letters (nucleotides). For purposes of illustration, alterations are made in the second position only although in fact they could occur anywhere.

is influenced by the sequential interaction of a sizable series of enzymes. Since enzymes are protein molecules, evidently many of them will be subject to direct genetic control, with mutations affecting their amino acid constituents.

Random variation in a morphological feature usually occurs in modifications of its growth process, and the commonest modification of the growth process is in the form of mutations affecting the controlling enzymes. At this level, the expected change is the alteration of a single amino acid, and almost invariably the result is either that the enzyme fails to work altogether, or that it does not work as well as it did in its unaltered form. If a growth enzyme fails to work, or works only to a reduced degree, then the structure which depends upon it either will fail to occur, or else will occur in reduced or only partially developed form. Stated briefly, the most likely effect of the most likely mutation will be the reduction of a structure which depends upon it; i.e. **the result of the probable mutation effect is structural reduction.** In a normally adapted organism, such reductions will of course be disadvantageous, on the other hand, wherever circumstances are altered so that a structure no longer has the same importance for survival that it previously had, one can predict that the probable mutation effect will produce its ultimate reduction.

Genetic Drift

If the importance of the probable mutation effect is minor in comparison with that of natural selection, then the importance of **genetic drift** is practically negligible. Basically, it is the **operation of chance influencing the distribution of characteristics in a sequence of generations.** This can easily be demonstrated by a simple example. Imagine a small, isolated band of Palaeolithic hunters—say, six men and six women—encamped in a rock shelter at the edge of a game-filled valley. Hunting is good, and since they are the only people in that part of the world, their future seems well assured. A noticeable peculiarity among the men is that, whereas four of them have a full head of hair (as did their fathers, even in advancing age), the other two, having inherited the tendency to become prematurely bald, sport at best only thinning patches of what once were long, healthy locks. On one unfortunate day the roof of their rock shelter caves in, crushing most of the band of hunters—several of the women, and all but two of the men. As luck would have it, both of the unscathed men are the balding ones. On the strength of this characteristic alone, one could safely predict that the future males of the band would tend to be bald as well. (Actually, this little example portrays a particular form of genetic drift called the **founder effect**—but it will nevertheless suffice to illustrate the logic of the general principle.)

Evidently it was sheer chance which affected the future of the male contingent of our little group. Sheer chance is a much more important element in determining proportions where a small group is concerned than with a large group. In a population of several thousand, for instance, the accidental loss of four men will not appreciably affect the relative proportions of characteristics transmitted to future generations, as it did in our example. Chance occurrences of this or any other sort cannot impart any consistent direction to evolution or account for an evolutionary trend. Since all major evolutionary developments are the result of forces which operate over very long periods of time, genetic drift is clearly of only local or incidental importance.

There are two reasons for mentioning genetic drift. First, it has been frequently invoked (too frequently, in fact) to account for changes which appear to have no adaptive significance. Second, throughout much of prehistory the characteristic human breeding population was just the sort of small, semi-isolated group in which genetic drift could have its greatest effect. While it is difficult to point with certainty to human features which owe their existence to the operation of genetic drift, it would be equally foolish to deny that this had played any role in human evolution.

Orthogenesis

Although **orthogenesis** is not really an evolutionary principle at all, it has been a prominent feature of former evolutionary schemes. It is considered here only so that it can be convincingly renounced. In the past, when evolutionary principles were dimly understood and did not seem adequate to account for the developments which the fossil record and contemporary organic diversity revealed, it seemed to some scholars that the visible evolutionary trends could be explained only by invoking mystical principles of unknown or supernatural guidance. Whether the forces invoked were cited as being "vital principles" or simply "evolutionary momentum," the result was the continuation of evolutionary development in a given direction for no obvious or logical reason. Straight-line development of this kind is what "orthogenesis" means.

There is no reason why development cannot occur in a consistent direction, provided that the selective forces which produce it continue to operate over long periods of time—and, clearly, this has happened in the evolutionary record. The main objections which the modern synthetic theory of evolution has to orthogenesis are to its inherent implications that there is an unknowable force involved, and that development, once started in a particular direction, will continue of its own momentum even after its initial stimulus has ceased to operate. As is now realized, evolution is completely opportunistic. It is simply **the accumulation of organic responses to continuing environmental stimuli.** When these stimuli cease, the responses cease as well. In this sense, then, we must deny that orthogenesis is a valid evolutionary phenomenon.

Man's Adaptation

Before embarking upon the final synthesis, wherein the foregoing insights are applied to the interpretation of the course of human evolution, we should give some attention to the age-old question, "What is man?" Definitions range from the realm of morality and philosophy to the pragmatic, functional, and physical. Depending on one's viewpoint, the more philosophical definitions can be characterized as displaying either dimensions of soaring insight or miasmas of vague verbalization. In any case, this realm will be left to other scholars with other purposes.

Attempts have been made to define man by means of specific, measurable, anatomical criteria, with the implication that such definitions are somehow "objective." In the eighteenth century an eminent Dutch naturalist distinguished man by the fact that he lacked an intermaxillary bone, and only within the last few years, anatomists have tried to claim that a brain capacity of at least 750 cc. is the minimum human criterion. The trouble with such criteria is that inevitable exceptions can be found, and that ultimately there is no necessary relation between them and the condition of being human. Definitions are created by man for his own convenience; although of great use, they are nevertheless arbitrary and subjective.

Viewed in evolutionary perspective, the most fruitful definition of man should be that which touches upon his most distinctive adaptation. Whereas arguments can be produced favoring the human brain in this regard, the social scientist can quickly counter this by pointing out that man does not survive by brain alone; however valuable it may be, brain does not serve as a substitute for experience. **The most unique characteristic of being human is the ability to profit from the accumulated and transmitted experience of other human beings.** This can be regarded as man's most important adaptation, and it is what the anthropologist means by the term **culture.**

It is important to realize that culture, as man's primary adaptive mechanism, is not a facet of human anatomy; in fact, some have referred to it as man's "extra-somatic adaptation." Evidently, any attempt to define humanity on the basis of anatomy alone will be doomed to failure. This is not to say that human anatomy is unrelated to culture; as we shall see, quite the reverse is the case. But the anatomical correlates to the fact of cultural existence are reflections of an already existing dimension, and must be regarded as being after the fact rather than of primary importance in and of themselves.

This ability to transmit information and experience from one individual to another and from one generation to another is most clearly recognizable in languages, and the records of their use. Unfortunately, however diagnostic language may be as an indicator of humanity, it leaves no trace in the archaeological or fossil record prior to the invention of writing—and, since the vast majority of the happenings in human evolution occurred prior to this event, this puts the prehistorian in the somewhat awkward position of trying to evaluate the humanity of our finds in the absence of the best criterion. Inevitably the only tangible evidence for prehistoric man's cultural capacity is prehistoric tools. This narrowing of the focus has even led some archaeologists to claim that the manufacture of tools should itself be the ultimate criterion of humanity, man being defined as a tool-making animal. One consequence of this has been a heightened concern for tool use, as opposed to tool manufacture, the feeling being that a creature which merely selected suitably shaped natural objects as tools does not deserve to be called "man." On the other hand, a creature which engaged in the regular modification of raw materials according to a set pattern could be appropriately elevated to the realm of the human. Contributing towards this appraisal was the fact that prehistoric stone tools can be traced back to the point where the amount of shape modification is so rudimentary that they are little more than selected hunks of rock. Some archaeologists have felt that at this point we reach the boundary between the human and the prehuman.

There are several reasons why this latter assumption should be greeted with scepticism. First, field observation shows that modern chimpanzees engage in a little simple tool manufacture. Next, merely because the prehistoric creature in question was perhaps not shaping stone does not necessarily mean that he was not shaping perishable materials which are manifestly easier to modify. Finally, the dichotomy between the simple selection of appropriately shaped raw materials and tool manufacture artificially creates categories out of what should be a whole zone of transition and which is unrelated to the question of whether or not the survival of the user depended upon the accumulated and transmitted experience of previous generations.

Properly speaking, the mere presence of shaped or unshaped tools in the archaeological record is of **symbolic** value. To the prehistorian they symbolize the fact that the user was utilizing a dimension of patterned behavior of an order of complexity which is too great to have been discovered anew each generation. Such behavior could be acquired only by **enculturation**—the process of growing up in a social environment conditioned by the accumulated and transmitted learning of previous generations. Given no more than this, we must recognize that, however rudimentary, the verbal clues, which undoubtedly assisted both the enculturation process and the activities which the presence of the tools symbolize, constituted a simple form of language. Furthermore, although our knowledge of the exact uses to which these early tools were put is rather limited, it is quite apparent that they were vital to the survival of the users.

With nothing more than the existence of stone tools, then, we can infer a creature which possessed culture in the anthropological sense, and which could not have survived without it. By our definition, such a creature deserves the designation "man."

Eight Culture
as an Ecological Niche

With the presence of stone tools considered as sufficient to establish the existence of a culture-dependent creature—man—then one must recognize the fact that some form of human being must have been in existence in the early Pleistocene, some 2 million years ago. The Pleistocene is the name for the geological period which contained the recently ended ice age. Since this was the period during which all of the major events of human evolution have taken place, necessarily it has been the focus for considerable attention on the part of the anthropological world.

Recently geophysicists have utilized a variety of ingenious techniques to establish the age of strata in the recent past. Recognizing that various radioactive elements "decay" into stable end-products at fixed rates, they have measured, in material taken from crucial geological layers, the ratio of certain of these radioactive elements to their end-products. Since the ratio discovered is proportional to the length of time during which the process has been going on, this serves as a measure of the time elapsed since the layer in question was formed. By these means, the Pleistocene has been calculated to extend from about 2 million down to some 10,000 years ago.

Perhaps we have made Pleistocene dating seem rather more simple than it is. Actually, there are a great many knotty problems connected with it. For instance, finding suitable mineral specimens to use for this kind of analysis is beset with difficulties. Indeed, only a very limited number of layers have been pinned down in this way; the rest have been tentatively fitted in by extrapolations based on the fossil animals contained. As a result, a great deal of uncertainty still remains concerning such problems as, for instance, the correlations and relative ages of layers in South Africa with those in Indonesia, or Europe with China. Despite all these uncertainties and inaccuracies, however, the temporal dimensions of the period during which man evolved are beginning to emerge.

During the Pleistocene there were four major onsets of glacial conditions in the Northern Hemisphere. Geologists used to regard this period as being entirely taken up by these glaciations and the milder intervening periods called **interglacials**, but recently the beginning of the Pleistocene has been extended back to include a long, mild stretch called the **Villafranchian**. The divisions of the Pleistocene and their approximate time durations are displayed in the chart.

DATE (years ago)	PLEISTOCENE DIVISIONS	GLACIAL STAGE	CULTURAL STAGE
10,000	Recent	Post (?) Glacial	Atomic Age / Neolithic
30,000	Upper Pleistocene	Würm	Upper Palaeolithic
			Middle Palaeolithic
100,000		3rd Interglacial	(Mousterian)
	Middle Pleistocene	Riss	Lower Palaeolithic.
			(Acheulian)
		2nd Interglacial	
		Mindel	(Abbevillian)
500,000		1st Interglacial	
	Lower Pleistocene	Günz	
	Villafranchian	Pre-Günz?	
1.75 million			
			(Oldowan)
4 million?			

The divisions of the Pleistocene showing the four major glacial stages with corresponding dates and cultural developments. Recently, evidence has been produced to show that a four- or even five-stage scheme may be much too simple. Note also that the time scale becomes increasingly compressed toward the early end.

The most consistent and reliable evidence for the existence of man throughout this time is to be seen in the form of chipped stone artifacts. The tool-making traditions practiced during the Pleistocene have been given the label **Palaeolithic** (old stone), and reveal the fact that the characteristic modes of subsistence were hunting and gathering. The change to a food-producing way of life did not begin to occur until after the Pleistocene was over. (Although this change surely was one of the most significant cultural events that ever occurred, treatment of it will be deferred until after the stages of human evolution have been considered.)

The Palaeolithic is further divisible into Upper, Middle (tentatively), and Lower segments of very unequal length. Ninety to 95 percent of man's time was spent in the Lower Palaeolithic, during which cultural change was extremely slow and cultural diversity apparently at a minimum. One says "apparently," since all we know of the Lower Palaeolithic is the few stone tools remaining and the bones of the animals on which men lived. While these indicate that the gross dimensions of human life were much the same from one end of the inhabited world to the other, yet it is perfectly possible and even likely that minor cultural differences of an unknown nature flourished in different areas. Stone tools form only a small component of the total cultural repertoire, which one should remember includes far greater quantities of perishable items and, even more important, dimensions of language, knowledge, and social behavior which leave no record. Potential diversity of this sort notwithstanding, however, it is still possible to state that major and basic facets of human adaptation were substantially the same from one end of the Old World to the other. Whether in South Africa, Europe, or Indonesia, game was hunted by the same techniques and processed by chipped stone tools which were virtually identical over vast areas.

The increasing local diversity visible in the stone tools of the Middle and Upper Palaeolithic will be treated later, but at the moment our concern is with the Lower Palaeolithic, and specifically with its earliest phases. According to current indications, the oldest cultural remains in the world, and consequently the earliest evidence for the existence of man, come from East and South Africa. The tools on which this judgment is based are of the crudest recognizable sort, and, were it not for the location in which they have been found, it would be almost impossible to prove that they were indeed the products of deliberate manufacture. But, occurring as they do by ancient lake margins and out on the plains miles from the nearest potential rock outcrop or natural source, one can only conclude that they were deliberately transported there. The discovery of such objects in a rocky stream bed or a wave-cut shore would excite no interest at all, for they are indistinguishable from the countless thousands of pebbles and cobbles which natural water action has battered and fractured. But found

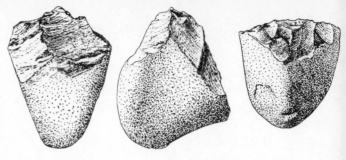

Pebble tools of the Oldowan type from Bed I of Olduvai Gorge, Tanzania. (By permission of the Trustees of the British Museum [Natural History].)

in a fine sedimentary deposit amidst the dismembered remains of extinct animals, they clearly indicate the activities of an ancient hunter.

In their crudest form, these early tools resemble river pebbles from which a flake or two has been knocked off, creating an edge or point. This is the source of the type designation by which they are known—"pebble tools." Because of the simple nature of the flaking, it is impossible to say whether it was done deliberately, or whether it had occurred naturally and the ancient hominid had simply chosen the stone from among others for this reason. The controversy over the importance of tool manufacture as distinguished from tool use has been mentioned in the preceding chapter. While this will probably never be resolved, the important thing to remember is that the presence of these tools, whether chosen or fashioned, signifies the presence of a creature whose life depended upon the behavioral complex of which these tools were a part, i.e., whose life depended upon the presence of culture.

There is another crucial fact to be realized, and that is that there is evidence for no more than one basic cultural tradition in the early Pleistocene. By tracing this up through time, it is evident that this tradition is the direct ancestor of all succeeding cultural traditions—which makes it, among other things, the remote parent of this book. A single original cultural tradition strongly suggests that only one organism developed culture as a necessary condition for its survival.

Ecology is the study of the life-ways of species, and the total life-way of a given species can be called its **ecological niche.** In the case of man, all facets of his way of living are conditioned by culture, and it is therefore justifiable to regard man as inhabiting a *cultural* ecological niche. There is another ramification of evolutionary theory which has been called the **competitive exclusion principle,** and this states that **no two organisms can continue to occupy the same ecological niche.** In a sense, this is stating the obvious, although, as in so much else, it is not always obvious until stated. The point is this: not only is culture a single ecological niche within which one would expect to find only a single species, but since there is only one cultural tradition visible in the early Pleistocene, the probability is greatly increased that there has been only one hominid species at any one time, and that the hominids of different time levels are lineally related.

56

It follows that if the dependence on culture can be demonstrated for more than one early Pleistocene form (form determined from the skeletal remains), then actual genetic relationship must exist, and it is the task of the student of human evolution to produce some scheme which will account for the observable diversity. We say again that the scheme here presented is not the only one available; it is developed extensively and to the relative exclusion of others principally because of its theoretical consistency. Because devoting equal space to the alternates would make this presentation overly long, they will simply be mentioned in passing.

Just as the evidence for cultural development can be viewed in terms of sequential stages, so can the picture of human physical development, although its stages are considerably more tentative because of the fragmentary nature of the record and the long time gaps between crucial specimens. For the earlier stages, the fossil evidence is spotty and widely separated, with the relative ages of the various localities bitterly contested. For most of the later stages the evidence is more complete, the dating more reliable, and the association with the cultural record more certain. In spite of this improvement, however, there are still many problems and disputed pieces of evidence, and many professional scholars are vehemently opposed to the implications of the solution about to be offered. Speculation is rife, and since no interpretation can be more than that, the best justification for the interpretation that follows is that it is consistent with both cultural and evolutionary theory.

Nine The Australopithecine Stage

Africa, which has provided us with the earliest archaeological evidence for human existence, has also yielded the earliest hominid skeletal remains. The term "hominid" is a colloquial version of the technical term *Hominidae*, the taxonomic family to which men belong. Man's closest relatives within the order *Primates* are the living anthropoid apes. These belong in the family *Pongidae*, which, together with the *Hominidae*, is included within the superfamily *Hominoidea*. To simplify matters of reference, the term "pongid" is generally used to designate anything which is more ape-like than man-like, while the term "hominid" is generally used to mean "taxonomically included within the family which harbors man himself."

The initial specimen, *Australopithecus africanus*, has given its name to a whole group of what are variously called "ape-men," "man-apes," "near-men," or even "primitive men." These include the Transvaal finds by Dart, Broom, Robinson, and others, and the category can also be extended to include the so-called Meganthropus finds of Java, Zinjanthropus and pre-Zinj of Olduvai Gorge, and the Koro Toro find from the southern

Sahara. Broom and others have attempted to elevate these to subfamilial status within family *Hominidae* and call them *Australopithecinae.* This would allow the retention of all the separate generic names as valid taxonomic units, but, in terms of the present analysis this course of action seems untenable. It is still useful to refer to the group as Australopithecines, and, as will be seen, they can properly be regarded as the first full stage in the evolution of man.

The differences of opinion concerning Australopithecine taxonomy revolve around the criteria that are considered important for purposes of classification. For Broom and Robinson, visually perceived differences and similarities are of prime importance, with taxonomic status depending on how many there are are of each. Thus the Australopithecines are ape-like in the possession of small brain cases, big molar teeth, facial projection, and a number of other features, but they differ from the apes in that they lack projecting canines,

Artist's conception of an Australopithecine. Note the simple look on his face and the long ape-like arms. This is sheer fancy since there is no way of telling facial expression from the fossil record, and there is no evidence that the arms were particularly long.

have a downward instead of a backward facing *foramen magnum* (hole at the base of the skull where the spinal chord enters), and have a shortened and expanded ilium (hip bone), and other related characteristics. In this latter regard they resemble humans more than apes, and Broom and Robinson (and others) consider that this balance of human and pongid features justifies a taxonomic position distinct from the one occupied by modern man, and of greater importance than merely either a specific or generic distinction. Note, however, that they can still be formally considered within family *Hominidae,* and hence they are called hominids.

Without denying that the balance of Australopithecine characteristics hangs somewhere between the pongid and hominid categories, it is worth pointing out that not all characteristics are of equal importance to the survival of the organism. It would seem that those characteristics which have the greatest adaptive significance should be the ones to determine the major taxonomic category. In the case of the Australopithecines, two characteristics outweigh all others, but it is not so much the characteristics themselves as what they signify. The first is the nonprojecting canine and the second is the fact that the Australopithecines were erect walking bipeds. Although these features have been recognized for years—in fact, they have largely contributed to the fact that the Australopithecines are generally included within the category hominid—their full significance has been only dimly perceived.

To take up the first of these, it is most suggestive that man and the Australopithecines, alone of all the terrestrial primates, do not have projecting canine teeth. Typically, terrestrial primates have greatly enlarged canines (witness the baboons), since, as small, relatively slow creatures, they could not survive the depredations of a variety of carnivores without some effective means of defense. The lack of an anatomical means of defense in man is obviously compensated for by his possession of a manufactured weaponry, and it is difficult to interpret the Australopithecines in any other light.

The other point to consider is the fact that the Australopithecines were bipeds, as can be seen from the anatomy of the pelvis and leg, and the placement of the skull. Admittedly it was fashionable in a generation gone by to envision the Palaeolithic hunter bounding across the grasslands on his long, straight legs, as though bipedalism were somehow the most efficient and "best" possible way of getting around. To any who may still harbor the lingering residue of such as illusion, I suggest that you seriously consider the vision summoned up by an irate adult *Homo sapiens* in hot pursuit of a thoroughly frightened *Felis domesticus* (house cat). As a mechanism for high-speed locomotor efficiency, hominid bipedalism is ludicrous. Obviously a creature which cannot even catch a small cat has even less chance of getting away from a large one, and it is certain that such felines as leopards and lions, as well as a variety of pack-hunting canines, must have posed a constant threat to the survival of any savannah-dwelling primate during the Pleistocene.

The only possible excuse for the development of hominid bipedalism is that it allowed for the development of compensating features (but clearly not formidable canines). Since the main functional correlate of bipedalism is the fact that the hands are freed from any involvement in the locomotor process, it would seem that they must have been used in wielding a nonanatomical defensive mechanism. Given a creature lacking dental defenses and pathetically slow on foot, we could postulate the existence of culture even *without* any direct evidence. However, culture does exist in the Lower Pleistocene. To be sure, there is a continuing debate as to whether the culture is really to be associated with the Australopithecines or perhaps with some as-yet-undiscovered "true man," but to postulate an undiscovered creator for the culture already known, and an undiscovered culture for the hominid in hand, seems unnecessarily complex, to say the least.

What with culture regarded as an ecological niche, and having evidence for only one cultural tradition in the lower Pleistocene, we should expect to find only one culture-bearing creature at that time. The Australopithecines clearly required a cultural adaptive mechanism in order to survive, and this author can see no reason not to regard them as the originators of the culture in question. Since this culture is also the lineal ancestor to all later cultural developments, it follows that the Australopithecines are lineal ancestors to all later hominids, including ourselves.

The taxonomic implications of this logic cast a doubt on the attempt to separate the Australopithecines from "true men" in their formal designations. If one regards taxonomic placement in terms of major adaptive characteristics, then one should consider the qualification for placement within genus *Homo* as being the possession of culture as a primary adaptive mechanism. Since one can deduce that the Australopithecines must have possessed culture, then it should follow that they belong in genus *Homo* as properly as do we, their direct descendants. If both the chimpanzee and the gorilla can be considered members of the same genus, as has recently been done, and if the lion and the pussycat are generically the same, then there should be reason enough to offer a single genus to include ourselves and the Australopithecines, particularly in view of their ancestral significance. This, however, is a point over which there is much heated debate. Suffice it to say that the controversy remains unresolved—and somewhat unimportant.

The problem of treating the diversity and distribution of the Australopithecines remains. Robinson has reduced the original bewildering profusion of generic designations to two, which he regards as being genus *Australopithecus* and genus *Paranthropus* and recently he has equated *Australopithecus* with *Homo*. Since the present treatment has further lumped them *all* within genus *Homo*, Robinson's distinction disappears at the generic level. The basis for making the distinction remains valid nevertheless, although it would appear that we do not yet possess sufficient evidence to grant it formal taxonomic recognition. For the present, these will be regarded as the Australopithecus and Paranthropus phases of the Australopithecine stage.

An early Australopithecine skull from Sterkfontein in the Transvaal region of South Africa. (Courtesy of the American Museum of Natural History.)

The Australopithecus Phase

This subdivision of the Australopithecine stage includes fossils from Taung, Sterkfontein, Makapansgat, and perhaps the pre-Zinj find from Olduvai Gorge. These constitute the oldest hominid remains known, although the correlation between the strata of East and South Africa is anything but certain and remains a major area of dispute. The most striking impression given by the individuals in this phase is their small size. Tentative estimates suggest a stature in the neighborhood of four feet and a bulk of between 50 and 80 pounds. This further strengthens the inference that culture must have been relied on for survival.

Brain size is scarcely more than one-third of the modern average, being in the neighborhood of 500 cc., which is right within the range of the modern anthropoid apes. Almost more than anything else, it has been this small brain size which has produced the controversy over the interpretations of the Australopithecines: for years, it has been an anthropological dictum that 750 cc. can be regarded as the absolute minimum required for normal human functioning. Since the Australopithecines obviously fall below this magic mark, it has been inferred that they could not possibly be the authors of the cultural tradition which existed at that time. On the other hand, it is difficult to make a direct equation between brain size and intellectual competence. The heights of genius in modern man have been attained by people whose brains have ranged from the vicinity of 1100 cc. to more than 2100 cc. (the average lies at approximately

1450 cc.). Although crude size must be of fundamental importance, it can be no necessary indicator of neurophysiological functioning. In addition, it should be remembered that the Australopithecines were distinctly smaller creatures than even those modern apes with brains of similar size. A male gorilla must range up to a quarter ton in gross bulk to warrant having a brain no larger than an Australopithecine which tipped the scales at a scant 100 pounds. It remains true, however, that the Australopithecine brain was well below the extreme lower border of the modern range of variation.

The dentition of the Australopithecus phase proper appears remarkably human. The palate is parabolic in form rather than being a parallel-sided U as in the anthropoid apes; the canines do not project (although they are still relatively large in proportion to the other front teeth); and the molars, while larger than their counterparts in modern man, have an entirely human cusp pattern. Yet relative tooth dimensions are an important clue to tooth function. It follows that, with the front teeth of the Australopithecus phase falling in the large end of the modern range of variation, and the molars starting within the modern range and considerably exceeding it, and considering their small body size, these early Australopithecines were much toothier creatures than any of the more recent hominids. Apparently the dentition was relatively more important to them than has been the case for their descendants.

The Paranthropus Phase

The later Australopithecines include the finds from the Transvaal sites of Swartkrans and Kromdraai; Meganthropus in Java; Zinjanthropus in Olduvai Gorge; Lake Natron; and possibly Koro Toro from the Chad area of the southern Sahara. The dating of these, as also of the earlier phase, is still the subject of a raging controversy. The most reliable and most complete sequence comes from the strata in Olduvai Gorge, Tanzania, where several absolute age determinations have been made on the basis of the proportion of Potassium 40 to its end product Argon—the famous Potassium-Argon (K/A) technique. While the Olduvai sequence is perhaps the most important in the entire picture of human prehistory, the problem is that there is virtually no agreement upon how it relates to the Transvaal sites in South Africa. Until the Potassium-Argon dates were produced, both areas were thought to represent deposits of early Middle Pleistocene times. However, now it appears, on the basis of absolute dating, that Olduvai is of Villafranchian age; this has been recently confirmed by a reappraisal of the remains of the fossil animals discovered there. This leaves the Transvaal nearly a million years out of phase.

However, the Middle Pleistocene date of the Transvaal involves a number of highly disputable assumptions, and, although the data and the logic are too specialized to warrant occupying space here, it is more than barely possible that the Transvaal sites should be considered Villafranchian as well. The presence of stone tools at Sterkfontein of the same type as those found in Bed I of Olduvai Gorge would lead one to suspect that comparable ages were likely even if there were no similar hominid remains to add to the suspicion. Against this, it has been claimed that the Transvaal hominids and cultural traditions represent the survival of archaic peoples and cultures in an isolated South African cul-de-sac while the rest of the world had long since advanced further along the path towards modern man. This is a frequently repeated argument, and it is worth devoting some time to its converse.

In the first place, it is difficult to imagine how a plains-dwelling creature could remain isolated for very long in South Africa when the grassland ecological zone in which it existed stretched unbroken up through that part of East Africa including Tanzania and continued on to the north. In the second place, if the Australopithecines were culture-bearing creatures, as it seems apparent they must have been, then one must apply the standard analysis of cultural dynamics to any consideration of the limitations or the extent of their habitation. One of the characteristics of peoples at a hunting and gathering level of subsistence is that they are highly mobile and range over extensive reaches of territory. As a result, they tend to penetrate to the extremes of the ecological zone in which they live. The great areal expanse of uniform tool-making traditions in the relatively better dated Middle Pleistocene serves as an example, and, by analogy, one would expect to find the same situation at an earlier level.

Tentatively, then, and in the absence of any conclusive evidence for or against it, the theoretical view here presented regards the Transvaal sites as of comparable age to those reliably dated in Olduvai Gorge. The same controversy has been raging over the dating of the Meganthropus remains from Java, and, for much the same reason, it is possible to regard these, too, as being late Villafranchian rather than Middle Pleistocene. One must recognize the fact that the absence of conclusive evidence equally allows some scholars to claim it possible that the South African Australopithecines survived into the Middle Pleistocene, where they were contemporary with more advanced hominids (the Pithecanthropines, perhaps). On the other hand, it must be realized that this can only be equally possible if the foregoing argument is no more likely than the argument that the Australopithecines were able to survive, cultureless, for more than a million

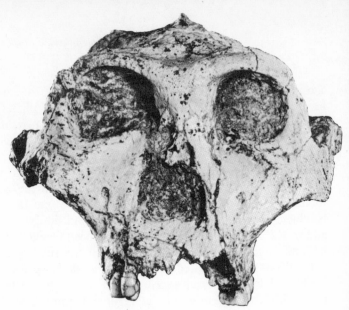

A *late Australopithecine of the Paranthropus type from Swartkrans in the Transvaal. (Courtesy of the American Museum of Natural History.)*

years despite their dental and locomotor deficiencies. The present claim, of course, is that this certainly is not equally likely and in fact is not likely under any circumstances.

The characteristics of the Paranthropus phase and its relationship to the preceding Australopithecus phase have yet to be considered. Physically, the members of the Paranthropus phase were at least twice as large, being approximately the size of modern man. In fact, the gross dimensions of the members of genus *Homo* have scarcely changed from that time to this. Brain size may have been less markedly enlarged, being perhaps in the neighborhood of 600 cc. This is somewhat difficult to tell, since the crushing and distortion consequent upon having been a million years or so in the ground means that exact reconstruction is not possible, and the restorations so far made may have been more than slightly influenced by the fact that those chiefly responsible have been devoted to interpretive positions rather different from that being presented here. It may be that Paranthropus represents no significant cranial advance over Australo-pithecus.

The fact should be pointed out that, within a given species, brain size is only partially related to body size, since, while a large member will in-deed have a larger brain than a small one, the relative increase in brain size is less marked than is that of body size. The average man, with a bulk one-third greater than the average woman, has a brain that is less than one-twelfth larger. The increases of gross size in a given species are accom-panied by increases in all the various organs and organ systems, but each of these increases at a different relative rate, a phenomenon described by

66

the term **allometry**. Allometric considerations are quite important when appraising organisms of markedly different sizes, but, as is apparent in some Australopithecine interpretations, have not always been given their due.

The remaining differences between Australopithecus and Paranthropus occur principally in the jaws, teeth, and related parts of their cranial anatomy. The incisors remain approximately the same size, but the canines, if anything, are slightly smaller in Paranthropus than in Australopithecus, while the molar teeth, particularly those towards the rear of the mouth, are significantly larger. Accompanying this enlarged crushing machinery is an expansion of the area allotted to masticatory musculature to the extent that the temporal muscles—one of the principal means of closing the jaws —rise up over the sides of the skull and meet at the mid-line. There, where the muscles of right and left come together, a flange of bone, the **sagittal crest,** arises to separate them and serve as a point of their origin. Although much has been made of the presence of the sagittal crest in the various representatives of the Paranthropus phase, its actual significance is simply as a reminder that, in the general increase in size, the facial skeleton and its operating musculature enlarge at a greater rate than the brain case to which they attach. The enlargement of the brow ridge, that bony bar above the eye sockets, is simply another reflection of this fact, and should no more evoke cries of "gorilloid" or "primitive" than does the sagittal crest.

Australopithecus, Paranthropus, and Adaptation

The significance of the difference between the two phases of the Australopithecine stage has yet to be treated. Robinson has produced a relatively involved explanation which requires a complicated series of ecological specializations, isolated survivals, invasions, and extinctions, apparently ignoring both allometry and adaptation. Hence he regards Paranthropus as a specialized vegetarian of dubious cultural capacity, representing a late survival of a **gerontomorphic** (primitive) form which could serve as a model for the ancestor of the earlier Australopithecus. Paranthropus then was presumably out-competed, or actively done in, by a "true man" of Pithecanthropine variety. Since there is no evidence that the Pithecanthropines existed back in the Villafranchian, Robinson has been doing his best to prove that Paranthropus really existed in the

Middle Pleistocene, but the evidence for this is no more satisfying. As the reader can easily appreciate, this runs rather counter to the present interpretive scheme.

In Robinson's view Australopithecus, with its lack of both brow ridge and sagittal crest, and its relatively smaller molars, is more "modern" in form. The fact that it has larger canines, even though they do not project above the occlusal level of the other teeth, is taken to indicate that Australopithecus was of a more carnivorous nature than the presumed Paranthropine vegetarians. Australopithecus, the hunter, presumably evolved directly into Pithecanthropus, which in turn dutifully extinguished the surviving Paranthropus relicts.

It would seem, however, that such an explanation is overly impressed with the "primitive" nature of large molar teeth, brow ridges, and sagittal crests. If one were simply to expand an Australopithecus to the size of a Paranthropus, the allometric adjustments would produce all the sagittal crests and enlarged molars necessary, and even more. It is not the larger molars of Paranthropus that are so remarkable; it is the fact that the whole front end of the dental arch did not expand along with the rest of the organism. That the incisors remain at the same absolute size as they had been in Australopithecus is actually a measure of their relative reduction, and the same thing is even more true of the canines. This, rather than molars and sagittal crests, would seem to demand some sort of explanation.

Explanation demanded, explanation produced. The search for Australopithecine precursors should ultimately produce a Pliocene ancestor, of closer pongid affinities, which had yet to develop culture as its principal adaptive mechanism. Such a creature must have possessed the normal primate means of ensuring its survival—i.e., an enlargement of the front end of the dental arch with a focus on projecting, defensive, canine teeth. As its cultural adaptation developed, however, the burden of self defense no doubt was transferred from teeth to tools, and the adaptive significance of the possession of such a dental arsenal was reduced and ultimately suspended. Over time, the operation of the probable mutation effect must have produced a reduction in the whole front end of the dental arch. Australopithecus, being closer to the Pliocene pongid ancestor, should show less reduction in the incisors and canines, relatively speaking, since the probable mutation effect would have been operating for a shorter period of time. Its continued operation, along with a general expansion in body size, could be expected to produce something very much like Paranthropus —and lo, Paranthropus appears!

The increase in body size which marks the attainment of the Paranthropus phase has been interpreted in relatively simple adaptive terms. The survival value of being 150 lbs. rather than under 100 lbs. may not be immediately apparent (especially if one thinks first of the number of additional calories per day which must be ingested to maintain the greater weight), but he who fights and gets away lives to eat the rest of the day, and the danger from civets, wildcats, jackals, and their ilk is much greater to a small primate than it is to a man-sized one, culture to the contrary notwithstanding. With a body bulk the equivalent to that of modern men, Parathropus must have had many fewer natural enemies than the preceding Australopithecus.

As a final facet of Australopithecine adaptations, some mention of locomotor efficiency should be made. The fact that they were erect walking bipeds has already been mentioned, but it appears that their bipedalism was somewhat less efficient than has been that of more recent hominids. This is not to say that they occasionally went down on all fours, which was certainly not the case, nor does it mean that an Australopithecine in full sprint was any slower than modern man. What is being referred to is their capacity for long-distance walking. Whereas the upper part of the Australopithecine pelvis, the **ilium**, is perfectly adapted to maintaining an erect trunk balanced above it (and, as such, is scarcely distinguishable from the modern), the lower part, or **ischium** (the part which we sit on), is elongated to such an extent that it is nearly half-way between the condition seen in the modern anthropoid apes and that of contemporary human beings. This elongation of the ischium to below the hip joint socket means that the muscles normally used in extending the leg attain greater leverage. At first thought one would be inclined to say, "Fine— more power to them!" Despite the bad pun, an elongated ischism does mean greater power of extension, but it also means that a greater amount of contraction is necessary to produce the same amount of action that a lesser contraction will produce where the muscles attach closer to the hip socket. If covering long distances without fatigue or energy depletion is of value, then the more efficient, if less powerful, shortened ischium is desirable.

One can infer from the Australopithecine pelvis that they had not quite acquired the long-distance capabilities of later hominids. Evidence from the late Australopithecine occupation sites in Olduvai Gorge suggests that their hunting capabilities were limited to the extent that they concentrated on small or slow creatures such as tortoises, lizards, rodents, and the helpless young of larger mammals. Presumably they also relied on large quantities of nuts, fruits, berries, wild vegetables, insects, and other gleanings including scavenging, but this is by way of inference from our knowledge of contemporary foraging peoples. In any case, they apparently did not engage in the regular, deliberate pursuit of large, herbivorous quadrupeds, and, possibly for this reason, long-distance locomotion was not perfected until the next stage of human evolution.

Before leaving the Australopithecine stage, some remarks should be directed towards the territories inhabited. Evidence for the Australopithecus phase comes only from Africa. Cultural remains are rudimentary, dating difficult, and skeletal evidence sketchy. Yet what there is of it suggests that man had his origins in Africa in the form which Dart originally called *Australopithecus africanus*. Our conclusion is that this properly belongs within the genus *Homo*, although the original specific designation may have reason to stand. The oldest known human would then be *Homo africanus*.

By the end of the Villafranchian or Lower Pleistocene, Australopithecus had long since evolved into Paranthropus, and the originally African locale had been expanded to include the entire tropics of the Old World. Pebble tools of late Villafranchian date extend from Cape Town to England, and from southwestern Europe via the Middle East and India to Southeast Asia and Indonesia. To date, hominid skeletal remains of this age and association have been discovered only in the Transvaal, Olduvai Gorge, the southern Sahara, and Java—and, at that, the Meganthropus finds of Java are only fragments of jaws and teeth. Nevertheless, the Paranthropus identity of all of these remains has not been shaken. With the extreme ends of the occupied range nailed down and relative cultural uniformity, at least as indicated by stone tools, throughout the area, it looms as highly probable that a single successful hominid, a Paranthropus type of Australopithecine, spread throughout the southern temperate and tropical parts of the entire Old World before the Middle Pleistocene, and provided the base for all subsequent human evolution.

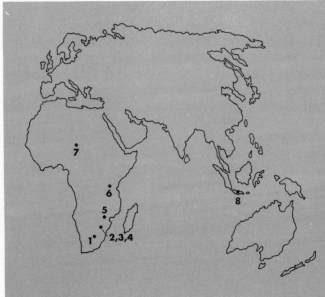

Location of Australopithecine sites. 1. *Taung*. 2. *Sterkfontein*. 3. *Swartkrans*. 4. *Kromdraai*. 5. *Makapansgat*. 6. *Olduvai Gorge*. 7. *Koro Toro*. 8. *Meganthropus (Java)*.

If the dating of 1.75 million years for Zinjanthropus in Olduvai Gorge is any sort of reliable clue to the age of the Paranthropus phase of the Australopithecines, then we are faced with a long temporal gap before we encounter the next stage of human evolution. Potassium-Argon dates from Olduvai Gorge, the Rhine terraces of western Europe, and the beds of Trinil age from Indonesia agree in roughly placing the scattered remains attributable to the Pithecanthropine stage at half a million years ago. No fossil hominids can be reliably placed in the zone between 0.5 and 1.75 million years, although continuity can be inferred from the unbroken cultural sequence archaeologically visible.

The most complete picture of the Pithecanthropine stage is based upon the fragments excavated from Choukontien, just southwest of Peking (Peiping), China, between the late 1920's and the beginning of the Second World War in the Far East. In terms of the Pleistocene glacial sequence, these date from the late second glaciation or early second inter-glacial. They were roughly contemporary with the remains which Dubois, and later von Koenigswald, discovered in Java and which give their name to the phase. Actually, von Koenigswald's Modjokerto infant and his so-called Pithecanthropus IV come from the Djetis layer underlying the Pithecanthropus-containing Trinil series, and may be considerably older. The fact that the adult, Pithecanthropus IV, has a more highly developed robustness of muscle marking, greater bone thickness, and noticeably larger molars than any other Pithecanthropine, is consistent with its greater age and serves as a possible pointer to an Austrapolithecine ancestry.

Using the Choukoutien Pithecanthropines as a general model for the form of the stage, two distinct differences can be seen when a comparison is made with the Australopithecines. First and most noticeable, the brain case is markedly larger, ranging up to twice as large. The Pithecanthropine range is from about 800 cc. to approximately

The Pithecanthropine Stage. *Note the artist's conception of early man as brutish and flea-bitten, clutching his "hand-axe." Again, this is purely imaginative. In fact we do not even know just how or for what purpose "hand-axes" were used.*

1200 cc., which places them all within the lower reaches of the normal modern range of variation. Their average of 1000 cc. is just about exactly half-way between ±500 cc. of the Australopithecines and the modern average of ±1450 cc. Despite the difficulty of drawing inferences from minor differences in brain size, the fact that body size remained the same as that of the Paranthropus phase, whereas brain size approximately doubled, cannot be devoid of significance. It is fair to guess that this represents a significant advance in intelligence, and it would seem further fair to suppose that this must have been of adaptive importance to survival within the cultural ecological niche.

The other anatomical difference is to be seen in the reduction of the molar teeth and associated facial skeleton. The heavy brow ridges remain and the front of the dental arch is unreduced, but the molars, with the exception of Pithecanthropus IV, are now within the upper limits of the modern range of variation. Extensive dismembered mammalian remains at Choukoutien reveal that the Pithecanthropines were hunting with an

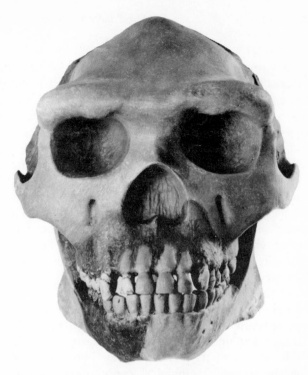

Pithecanthropus IV as reconstructed by Dr. Franz Weidenreich. The dark parts are original and the light, reconstruction. The whole back part (not visible) was preserved. Recent finds in Java and China have confirmed the accuracy of Weidenreich's reconstruction. (Courtesy of the American Museum of Natural History.)

effectiveness beyond the Australopithecine level, with the result that meat must have been a regular and significant item in the diet. The amount of mastication necessary to reduce animal protein to digestible form is far less than is true for vegetable products. Ruminants are forced to chew, chew, and rechew their food so that a thorough mixture with salivary enzymes will assure its digestibility. A quick look at the molars of a cat, however, will demonstrate that shearing rather than crushing is their main function. For a carnivore, the main purpose of the molars is to reduce their food to swallowable size, since animal protein does not require extensive salivary enzyme action before it can start to be digested in the stomach. If our Pithecanthropines were eating significantly greater quantities of meat than their Australopithecine forebears, then they should have had less need for the great crushing molars of the Villafranchian forms. With molar size free to vary, then the probable mutation effect could do its work, with the result that reduction took place. Critics may cry that this smacks of facile explanation, but, at the moment, no alternative suggests itself.

The evidence for successful hunting also suggests that the pelvis had finally completed its modification to allow for relatively effortless long-distance walking. Unfortunately, the skeletal evidence is too fragmentary to afford direct confirmation of this, although since the femur (thigh bone) is virtually indistinguishable from that of modern man, one can offer this as tentative confirmation. The human adaptation to long-distance locomotion is actually fairly remarkable in its own right, although, considering the flabby physique of the average reader in his armchair, it is perhaps less easy to appreciate this than it should be. As an example of what a well-conditioned human being is capable of, one can cite the mode of hunting practiced even today by certain peoples. This involves literally walking one's quarry into the ground. South African Bushmen, American Indians, and Australian Aborigines are noted for this simple, if rather exhausting, technique. The hunter takes up the trail of a large herbivore and keeps it moving until out of sheer fatigue it can go no farther, at which point the hunter moves in and dispatches it. The process may actually drag out over a number of days, involving a skill in tracking, and a degree of patience and endurance, difficult to conceive for the beneficiary of the technology of this mechanized age.

Two physiological facets aid the hunter in this form of activity. First, a large herbivore depends upon the ingestion of great quantities of food of relatively low nutritive value, which means that it has to spend a considerable portion of its lifetime eating. The hunter, on the other hand, fortified by occasional nibbles of concentrated nourishment in the form

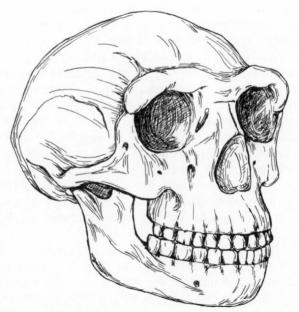

A composite reconstruction made under the direction of Franz Weidenreich and based upon the Pithecanthropine fragments found at Choukoutien, near Pekin. Originally called Sinanthropus pekinensis.

of dried meat products, nuts, and other high-quality edibles, can keep pushing on without stopping, prodding his quarry along just fast enough · so that it does not have an adequate chance to replenish itself, and, in a couple of days, his patience will be rewarded.

The second physiological fact involves the human ability to dissipate metabolically generated heat. Man, with his hairless skin richly endowed with sweat glands, can continue to function effectively throughout the heat of the day. The South African Bushmen capitalize on this fact by running down large quadrupeds in the middle of the day when the animals are prone to develop heat exhaustion if they attempt any continued rapid locomotion. In the tropics, mammalian life usually reposes in the shade during the hot part of the day. It is not without significance that all of the predatory carnivores which survive as a result of the active pursuit of prey engage in their maximum expenditure of energy in the relative coolness of the early morning or late afternoon and evening. Except for mad dogs, man alone goes out in the noonday sun, nor is this a peculiarity of the English, either. It would appear that the development of human predation long ago capitalized on the limitations which a coat of fur has placed upon mammalian activity during the heat of the tropical day, and one can suspect that the perfection of the hominid pelvis for long-distance walking was accompanied by the effective loss of human body hair. At the same time, the intensity of ultraviolet radiation poses something of a problem to the hairless tropic-dweller, since it greatly increases the chances of developing skin cancer. The solution is the development of a concentration of the protective pigment **melanin.** To follow up the train of these observations with a further speculation, it is possible to postulate that with the development of effective hunting techniques, somewhere in between the Australopithecine and the Pithecanthropine stages, man became hairless and black. Later we will account for the depigmentation which occurred in the background of some of the world's peoples, but at present it is sufficient to suggest that all of mankind passed through a heavily pigmented stage.

The deposits at Choukoutien reveal something else in the human behavioral repertoire which may be of great significance: fire. Charcoal accumulations which must have been built up over considerable periods of time suggest that the inhabitants of the local caves must have been able to control fire. However, although this is tantalizing "evidence" for the human use of fire (and the earliest such use thus far known), the problem is that there is no confirmatory evidence from other sites of the same age. The next tentative "evidence" for the human use of fire appears only later in the second interglacial, and elsewhere, at that.

Since the subject of evidence for the human use of fire in prehistoric times is of some importance, it is worth exploring its implications. For one thing, such evidence is a boon to the prehistorian, since it means that the difficulties involved in discovering the remains of ancient habitations are greatly reduced. With the advent of fire, caves were inhabited by man for the first time—a fact which greatly reduces the number of places the archaeologist has to investigate before getting results. Prior to the advent of fire, caves were studiously avoided at night by prehistoric man, since they were more in the nature of traps than shelters. The keen visual sense which man inherited from his arboreal precursors, although remarkable in its acuity of color discernment and depth perception when light is provided, left (and still leaves) him relatively helpless in dim light, and practically disoriented in total darkness.

Fire is useful in three ways, and symbolic of a fourth phenomenon of considerable importance. It provides light, which extends the length of time during which a hominid can effectively operate. It provides nocturnal protection, which can convert the limiting confines of a cave into a safe area of refuge. And it provides warmth, which can enable a fundamentally tropical mammal to extend its range into colder climates normally closed to it. The final thing, that which fire symbolizes, is related to the reuse of an agreed-upon campsite. If the deposits at Choukoutien indicate an area which was intermittently used again and again, or even for a succession of days, then it is more than just likely that the users were capable of communicating time and place between each other. With this as a possibility, the ability of the group to divide up, agreeing to meet later at the camp, is also a possibility, and we must recognize in this the origins of the division of labor. Because of the physiological differences between males and females—the latter being charged with the care of infants and young —the most basic form of the division of labor is inevitably by sex, with the men concerned more specifically with the chase and the women concentrating on vegetable products and slow game. Even such a rudimentary division of labor as this can greatly increase the subsistence base of a foraging group; its effectiveness is evident in the fact that it is still characteristic of the remaining hunting and gathering peoples. Granting that this is rather a jump from the simple recognition of campsites via reused hearths, it nevertheless seems a legitimate interpretation to offer for a creature for whom specialized hunting activities had begun to play an increasingly important role in group subsistence.

Yet to be considered is the formal taxonomic designation of the Pithecanthropines and their geographic distribution. The controversy which raged over the status of the original Pithecanthropus around the turn of the century now belongs to history, although one or two professional scholars still would like to see it recognized as representative of a side line which became extinct without issue. Although a great many anthropologists balk at accepting the Australopithecines for one reason or another, most are willing to regard the Pithecanthropines as genuine human beings who were ancestral to all later forms of men. As a result, the validity of the term *Pithecanthropus* as a formal generic designation has been questioned, and most authorities now regard them as belonging within genus *Homo*. The original specific designation is still considered tentatively valid, and many workers are quite happy in referring to the Pithecanthropines as *Homo erectus*.

Inferences concerning the geographic distribution of these early men are greeted with a noticeably lower level of enthusiasm. A generation ago, when they were unchallenged as the oldest hominids known, and when they were recognized only in Java and China, there was a general feeling that Asia had been the cradle of mankind. Now, however, with Africa possessing the strongest claims to be the initial human homeland, there is much more willingness to view the Pithecanthropines as having spread throughout the area which the archaeological remains indicate was inhabited by man, rather than to regard them as having been restricted to one small province. New finds, and the reappraisal of an old one, provide confirmation for this suspicion. Robinson now regards the Swartkrans finds, which he and Broom originally called *Telanthropus*, as being a proper Pithecanthropine, and, although the brain case is lacking, the jaws and teeth would appear to prove him right. (He goes on to assume their contemporaneity with Paranthropus on grounds which, as has already been mentioned, have yet to be justified.)

Sites of major Pithecanthropine discoveries. 1. Pithecanthropus (Java). 2. Sinanthropus (Choukontien). 3. Heidelberg. 4. Ternefine. 5. Rabat. 6. Telanthropus. 7. Olduvai Gorge. 8. Verteszöllös (Hungary).

One problem with trying to identify possible Pithecanthropines on the basis of jaws and teeth and not much more is the fact that they are indistinguishable from Neanderthal jaws and teeth. With no more skeletal evidence available, the nod as to which stage gets assigned is determined by dating. If the form is second glacial or second interglacial, jaws and teeth of Pithecanthropine size can be comfortably referred to the Pithecanthropine stage. An example is the famous Heidelberg mandible of 1907. The teeth correspond quite nicely to those discovered at Choukoutien, and, since the dating can be fixed at an interstadial of the second glaciation, it is reasonable to infer that Heidelberg represents the northwesternmost extreme of the Pithecanthropine range, just as Telanthropus may represent the southwesternmost extreme—although the unproven date of the latter reduces our certainty. Jaws, teeth, and a few cranial fragments from Ternefine, Algeria, apparently belong to the right time range also, and hint at the continuity from Germany to the Transvaal.

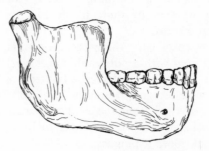

The Heidelberg jaw. Until the recent discovery of the back end of a skull and a couple of deciduous teeth at Vérteszöllös in Hungary, this was the oldest human fossil known from Europe.

As a final note on Pithecanthropine distributions, Leakey's finds in Bed II of Olduvai Gorge are of really great importance. Whereas Telanthropus, Ternefine, and Heidelberg were jaws without heads, the 1960 find is a head without a jaw, but the skull is as Pithecanthropine in shape as it can be: heavy brow ridges, sloping forehead, great constriction behind the brows (post-orbital constriction), yet with a brain of substantial enough size to be unquestionably regarded as human. Of further importance, a Potassium-Argon date can be assigned of roughly half a million years, providing a comforting confirmation of the equivalence of the western with the eastern versions of the Pithecanthropine stage. In addition, among the 1963 finds there are two complete mandibular tooth rows and one nearly complete maxillary (upper jaw) tooth row, as well as a variety of cranial vault fragments. Measurements are not yet available, but the published pictures appear to further confirm the Pithecanthropine estimation (despite Leakey's "*Homo habilis*") for the dentition as well as the skull.

Of an importance at least as great is the association of the Olduvai Pithecanthropines with a stone tool-making tradition which the underlying layers show to have evolved without break from the pebble tools

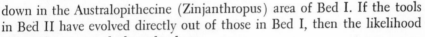

Pithecanthropine skull-cap from site LLK in Bed II of Olduvai Gorge, Tanzania. (Photo by Dr. L. S. B. Leakey, © National Geographic Society.)

down in the Australopithecine (Zinjanthropus) area of Bed I. If the tools in Bed II have evolved directly out of those in Bed I, then the likelihood is greatly increased that the hominids in Bed II evolved directly from the type represented in Bed I.

The transition from Bed I to Bed II at Olduvai shows the development from the pebble tools of the Oldowan tradition into the Middle Pleistocene tools worked on two faces—bifaces or "hand-axes"—which are so important in Africa, Europe, the Middle East, and parts of India up to the last glaciation. Interestingly enough, a biface tradition never develops in Middle Pleistocene deposits from the eastern half of India east into China, Southeast Asia, and Indonesia. Instead, pebble tools of essentially Oldowan type continue right on up to Upper Pleistocene, which witnesses the influx of a much more elaborate technology. This maintenance of what can be considered eastern and western cultural traditions through-

A biface from St. Acheul in northwestern France, the location which gave its name to a whole category of middle Pleistocene tools.

out the Middle Pleistocene has interesting implications for both the nature of the development of the stages of human evolution and the relationship of the geographical areas.

The initial spread of Australopithecines of the Paranthropus phase from Africa throughout the rest of the Old World tropics was obviously in the nature of an actual movement of people—even if this only involved the excess population of locally established groups budding off and inhabiting the next territory just a few miles away. However, once the habitable world was occupied, development from the Paranthropus phase to the next full stage and the succeeding ones was something which probably occurred gradually and simultaneously throughout the entire occupied world (rather than at one point, after which it would presumably spread by extinguishing the conservative local inhabitants, wherever they might be). After the initial Paranthropus spread, invasions of any note probably did not occur until the time of the great population imbalances and technological disparities which grew out of the food-producing revolution.

The reason for this view can be seen in appraising the nature of the cultural adaptive mechanism. This may seem like something of a contradiction, coming right after statements recognizing the difference between the Eastern and Western cultural traditions, but the answer is that significant cultural adaptations can and do diffuse with ease across the boundaries of specific cultures. The bow and arrow, for instance, diffused to most of the corners of the globe in a relatively short period of time, and the documented spread of the use of tobacco indicates a rate of diffusion and a disregard for cultural boundaries which is nothing less than phenomenal. With the high degree of mobility and relative cultural uniformity (functionally) characteristic of the Lower Palaeolithic, any significant advance in hunting technique, food preservation process, or the like must have diffused quite rapidly throughout the inhabited world—accompanied by the inevitable if not large leakage of genes across population boundaries as well. With the major forces shaping man's evolution heavily influenced by major cultural adaptations, and with the latter effectively diffused, whatever their local origins, during the Lower Palaeolithic, then one can postulate relative similarity in the selective forces operating on man. Similar forces would have produced similar evolutionary consequences in widely separate areas, even without an accompanying slow genetic interchange, although this must have occurred as well.

The similarity which this explanation bears to the one recently offered by Coon has been remarked upon by more than one scholar, but Coon views the advances from one evolutionary stage to another as having taken place in isolation and at different rates of speed in different localities. The present presentation, on the other hand, views the diffusion of the cultural *reasons* for the specific physical changes which characterize the stages as having been rapid enough so that the unity of the human species was maintained at any one time. Development from one stage to the next, then, would have proceeded at approximately the same time and the same rate throughout the inhabited world. The probability that a given population will be genetically more like its precursors in the same locality is of course greater than the probability that it will be genetically closer to groups in adjacent areas, and this allows for the development of regional peculiarities, but, at the same time, genetic material is continually being exchanged with adjacent areas. The result is that no human population has ever become different enough from the others to warrant taxonomic recognition.

Once again, observation of contemporary representatives of a hunting and gathering form of subsistence economy provide evidence which reinforces this suspicion. Among these people, exogamy—seeking mates from other unrelated groups—rather than endogamy or inbreeding, is a virtually universal phenomenon. This greatly increases the possibilities not only for gene flow from group to group but also for information transfer as well. Not until local populations became sedentary, following the development of a food-producing subsistence economy, did group endogamy become a phenomenon to be reckoned with.

Eleven The Neanderthal Stage

Before plunging into the Neanderthal stage proper, there are a few finds which occur in the gap between the Pithecanthropines and the Neanderthals. Although the gap is long (one-third to half a million years) and the finds relatively few in number, a great deal of attention has been paid them, and they are the source of much disagreement and controversy. Because they are fragmentary, distorted, or incomplete, the assessment of their form is a matter of interpretation: depending upon the theoretical gambit preferred by whichever scholar is doing the interpreting, they have been used to support diametrically opposed schemes of human evolution. In reality, however, the fragments are not sufficiently complete to "prove" *anything* more than the mere fact that man was in existence during this time (a point which the increasingly rich archaeological record is more than adequate to demonstrate). Nevertheless, because of the importance which has been claimed for some of them, a few words will be devoted to their consideration.

The three pre-Neanderthal fragments which are most frequently referred to are those from Steinheim, Swanscombe, and Fontéchevade, to name them in order of their discovery. The oldest of these "skulls" is the Swanscombe skull, which is considered reliably dated to the latter part of the second interglacial. The pieces of this skull were discovered in a gravel pit of the lower Thames River in southeastern England, with the three major fragments constituting the rear of the cranial vault being unearthed in 1935, 1936, and, by an almost impossibly rare piece of good fortune, in 1955. At the time when the initial pieces were found, British anthropologists, because of their long-standing lack of enthusiasm for facing the possibility that man may have had a Neanderthal ancestor, were desperately eager to find evidence for the existence of men of modern form at an earlier time level than that attributable to the Neanderthals. As a result, modern features were stressed whenever possible, and, in the case of Swanscombe, with the all-important facial parts missing, opinions concerning its status could be promoted without much risk of encountering solid objections from any quarter whatsoever. By default, then, Swanscombe has been regarded as modern ever since.

A Neanderthal. *The classic "cave man," leopard skin, club, and all, dimly peering at a world which is largely beyond his comprehension. In fact, the Neanderthals probably had much more effective weapons and clothing, and there is reason to believe that they were at least as intelligent as modern men, if not more so.*

Despite the fact that the back end of the skull is relatively nondiagnostic in the assessment of the major distinguishing characteristics of evolutionary stage, there are some features which generally accompany those of diagnostic significance, and it is not without interest to discover some of these on the Swanscombe skull. For instance, the greatest width is far back and low down on the skull, and the skull height is remarkably low in proportion to it. The width across the occipital bone alone is greater than 99.9 percent of comparable modern skulls, and the bones are remarkably thick. There are other indications as well which locate the Swanscombe skull right in the middle of the characteristic Neanderthal range of variation, but, lacking the crucial frontal bone and attached facial parts, we are not at liberty to do more than suspect that these parts may well have agreed with the indications of the vault. Unequivocal interpretation of Swanscombe is not possible, but, in marked contrast to the majority of the claims put forward on its behalf, it most certainly provides no evidence whatsoever for the existence of men of modern form in the Middle Pleistocene.

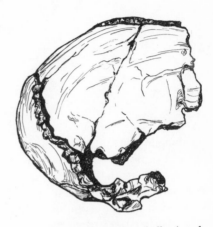

The Steinheim skull, found two years earlier in a gravel pit near Schiller's birthplace, not far from Stuttgart in western Germany, would at first consideration seem to be a more promising subject for interpretation than the Swanscombe skull. The date is roughly the same, being late second interglacial or early third glacial, and the skull is relatively compete, with much of the face preserved. Yet the arguments

The Swanscombe skull viewed from the right side.

surrounding the attempt to establish its significance show no sign of diminishing. The skull is small and low, with a cranial capacity of approximately the Pithecanthropine average; the brow ridge is a formidable bony bar, but the back is rounded and smooth, suggesting modern form; the third molar is markedly reduced. Although the modern form of some of the other parts of the face has also been stressed, there are two principal difficulties in the way of definitive interpretations. First, the whole lower front part of the face is missing, leaving only the molars and one premolar at the rear of the dental arch. This is particularly to be regretted since the most crucial features distinguishing modern from Middle Pleistocene morphology are those centered upon the forward end of the dental arch. The second difficulty lies in the distortion which the skull has undergone. The whole left side of the skull is crushed towards the mid-line, reducing the width of the base to less than that ever recorded for a normal modern individual (where the width of the base tends to be less than for Middle Pleistocene individuals in the first place). The palate has been reduced in width, and the whole of the facial skeleton has been pushed slightly back underneath the skull. As a result of the missing and distorted aspects, it is evident

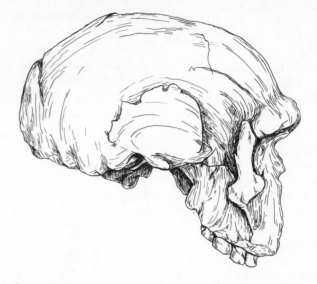

The Steinheim skull.

that no unequivocal judgment can be made. Yet, with its small cranial capacity and heavy brow ridge, it can tentatively be regarded as belonging somewhere between the Pithecanthropines and the Neanderthals.

The other principal fragments for which the cry of "ancient moderns" has been raised are those found in the cave at Fontéchevade in the Department of Charente in southwestern France. The discovery of pieces of two human skulls was made in 1947 and widely hailed by the anthropological world as proof at long last of the existence of man of modern form back in the Middle Pleistocene. Closer examination of the circumstances of the discovery and their nature, however, reveals a monumental amount of confusion. As it turns out, one of the skull fragments was not found *in situ* but in the laboratory where the block of material containing it had been brought for dissection at greater leisure. This fragment includes the section of a skull towards the medial part of the left eye-socket, between the eyes, and rising a short distance up the forehead. From what one can see, it is apparent that no heavy brow ridge was present, but, also from what one can see, there is no assurance that the fragment came from an adult. It is just as consistent to regard it as a juvenile from a population among which heavy brow ridges developed during adolescence.

The second Fontéchevade fragment includes the better part of the top of the cranial vault of what was apparently an adult; however, the diagnostic frontal and basal parts are missing, the piece is crumbly, and so much doubt clings to the attempts to project a reconstruction from the available parts that it would be far better to put the finds aside until more complete evidence is discovered. Certainly, at the moment, the only reason for stressing the dubiously "modern" features of Fontéchevade, or Swanscombe or Steinheim for that matter, is the desire which so many authors apparently have to find something less "primitive" which came before the

Neanderthals of the last (Würm) glaciation, thereby proving that the latter could not possibly be the ancestors of recent mankind. This desire seems to have its roots in a trend of thinking which becomes alarmed whenever the suggestion is raised that modern man evolved from something less man-like than himself.

In the generation just recently past, the extreme proponents of this view denied ancestral status to virtually all fossil hominids which differed in any way from modern man, claiming at the same time that the true modern ancestor had yet to be found, or advancing the candidacy of now one, now another questionable specimen. The original Neanderthaler, having been found just at the time when evolution was becoming a major issue, was the subject of so much critical suspicion that, even today, the lingering vestige of this tends to be applied to the whole stage to which it gave its name. In the absence of any clear support, however, the old view is becoming increasingly difficult to maintain.

There are a few other fragments reliably dated to the time interval between the Pithecanthropine and the Neanderthal stages, but, since these are mainly jaws and teeth, and the dental apparatus is approximately the same in both stages, it is not possible to infer much of evolutionary significance from them. Time has come, then, to discuss the Neanderthals themselves.

Of all the human fossils known, Neanderthals have generated the most public interest, serving as the prototype of the cartoon cave man. Somewhat ironically, now that the reading public has finally gotten to the point where it is willing to accept the hominid record as indicative of the course of human evolution, it is the professional anthropologists who have tended to become uneasy at the possibility of discovering a Neanderthal skeleton in the *sapiens* closet. However, if one accepts the Pithecanthropines as being a stage in human evolution, it is difficult to get from there to modern form without going by way of something which must be regarded as Neanderthal. Add to this the occurrence of Neanderthals in some quantities in the time immediately prior to the earliest reliably dated appearance of men of modern form, and the probability that the Neanderthals were the ancestors of ourselves is greatly increased.

Prehistoric research has been going on longer in western Europe than anywhere else, so it is no surprise to discover that more Neanderthal remains have been discovered there than anywhere else—starting with the first recognized specimen in 1856 which gave its name to the whole stage. In spite of this it has taken the better part of a century for the various areas of interest which constitute the science of prehistory to mature. In the meantime, many discoveries have been made which could not be adequately treated because of the limitations of the times: stratigraphy was not controlled, faunal or cultural associations were not recorded, absolute dates could not be determined, and so on. Consequently, despite the quantity of Neanderthal material from Europe, virtually none of the major specimens can be precisely placed in time. The best we can do is associate them with the Mousterian tool-making tradition which, in turn, can be dated from approximately 35,000 years ago back to the beginning of the last glaciation or the late third interglacial some 100,000 years ago. However, direct dating of Neanderthal skeletal material has been made at two sites in the Middle East, one in Palestine (Tabūn) and one in Iraq (Shanidar), and both agree, on the basis of C_{14} determinations, in assigning an age of a little more than 40,000 years. No known Neanderthals are more recent than this, and the evidence suggests that many are much older, so it is fair to use this date as the tentative boundary for the most recent occurrence of the stage as a whole. For the beginning of the stage, specimens are few and fragmentary, and since they belong to a period too old to be dated by C_{14} and too young to be dated by K/A, there is more than a little uncertainty remaining.

To consider the form of the Neanderthals, one must start by dispensing with the hairy, slouching, bestial image, tramping through the Ice Age snow drifts clad only in a loincloth, and not quite able to stand erect. While there are minor differences in the pelves of the known Neanderthals from those of modern men, there is no evidence to indicate that their

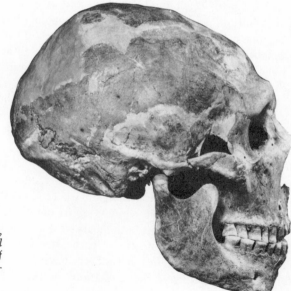

The skull of Shanidar I, a classic Neanderthal from Iraq. (Courtesy of the Iraq Museum, Baghdad.)

posture was any less erect than that of ourselves. The human line has stood upright since the Australopithecine stage, and any attempt to inflict the Neanderthals with a "bent-knee" gait is simply a survival of the efforts on the part of early interpreters to view all aspects of Neanderthal anatomy as being "primitive" or ape-like. (This also involves the incorrect assumption that apes cannot straighten their legs at the knee.) From the neck on down, the only difference between Neanderthal and modern is the indications of generally greater ruggedness in Neanderthal joints and muscles. This is more an average difference in degree rather than one in kind.

Above the neck, however, it is a different story. To be sure, the cranial measurements of some Neanderthals do not surpass those of some moderns, but there are other Neanderthals which present an array of dimensions which cannot be matched in recently living people. These revolve around the dentition and associated facial areas where the Neanderthals do not differ functionally from the Pithecanthropines. All told, the Neanderthals are distinguished from the Pithecanthropines by the possession of brain cases of fully modern size, while they are distinct from modern men in the possession of Pithecanthropine dentitions and faces. In fact, the Neanderthal front teeth include the largest to be found in the whole picture of human evolution, although this may simply be due to the scarcity of specimens from the earlier stages.

Some people have regarded it as puzzling that the human brain should have attained full size 100,000 years ago (even more if their interpretations of Swanscombe are correct) and remained the same ever since. The argument has been advanced that, if intelligence has survival value, more intelligence should have greater survival value. This, however, is failing to recognize that "survival of the fit" is a more appropriate expression than "survival of the fittest," and that man's primary adaptive mechanism is **culture.** When culture had developed to the point where the knowledge and traditions transmitted would confer an adequate chance for survival on any who could master it, the advantage of being yet more intelligent became relatively unimportant. Although one could argue that an innovator must have more intelligence than a person who is just able to master the culture in which he is brought up, it still remains true that the dullest member of a group benefits from the innovations of the brightest to an equal extent, and that genetic endowments are passed on to the next generation with the proportions unchanged. In the face of such an explanation, it would be surprising to find an *increase* in cranial capacity during the last 100,000 years.

As a tentative definition of Neanderthal, this has been offered: "Neanderthal man is the man of the Mousterian culture prior to the reduction in form and dimension of the Middle Pleistocene face."

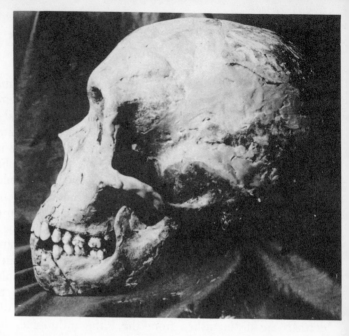

The Le Moustier skull, a classic Neanderthal from western Europe. (Courtesy of the American Museum of Natural History.)

As we have said, culture at this level of complexity accounts for the cessation of the increase in brain size, and when we deal with the development of modern form, we shall see how it also accounts for the reduction of the human face. At the moment, however, it is worth paying some attention to the cultural remains themselves, and the implications they contain.

The term **Mousterian** comes from the village of Le Moustier in southwestern France where the type site is located. Tools of Mousterian form are distributed throughout western and southern Europe, south of the Balkans, east into the Middle East, and northeast through the Crimea, the Caucasus, and Uzbekistan. Throughout this whole area, which one could call a Mousterian culture area, there was a whole series of bands possessing related cultures, and between which similar culture elements maintained circulation. Local differences in details of typology and technique of manufacture persisted, but all these subcultures possessed the same functional tool categories: scrapers, points, and knives.

Scrapers indicate a concern for the preparation of animal hides, which is reasonable for people living in a subarctic climate. It used to be thought that effective clothing was not developed until the ensuing Upper Palaeolithic, with the invention and manufacture of bone needles, but there is no reason to deny the Neanderthals the use of skin clothing just because they had no needles: wrapped clothing bound on by thongs was utilized by the poorer peoples of Europe right up to recent historical times. Certainly the Neanderthals must have been doing something with the skins they prepared, and it is reasonable to suppose that the manufacture of clothing was one such thing.

90

The Mousterian points, made on flakes of a variety of sorts, evidently were frequently hafted, and the inference can be made that spears were being so tipped. Whether these were thrusting spears or throwing spears

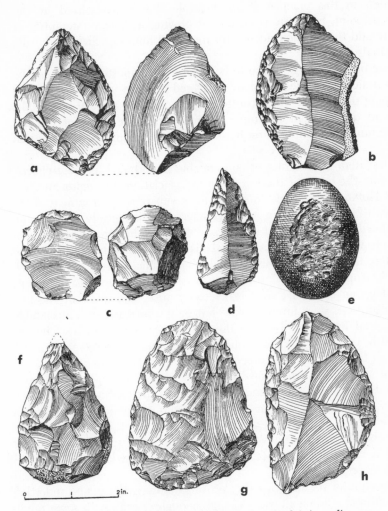

A collection of Mousterian tools. a, b, side-scrapers (racloirs), c, disc-core, and d, point, from rock-shelter at Le Moustier near Peyzac (Dordogne); e, small anvil- or hammerstone (pebble of ferruginous grit), Gibraltar caves; f, hand-axe from Le Moustier; g, hand-axe (chert), and h, oval flake-tool (flint), from Kent's Cavern, Torquay. a–d. Typical Mousterian; f, Mousterian of Acheulian tradition; g, h, of Acheulo-Levalloisian tradition. (By permission of the Trustees of the British Museum, [Natural History].)

we have no way of knowing, but they obviously played an important role in the Neanderthal way of life. One might make the comment that the complex and precisely coordinated activities associated with throwing is a uniquely human phenomenon, no other animal attaining any degree of effectiveness in this practice at all. Possibly this is symbolized by the Mousterian point, but there is no way of proving it, however tempting it may be to add this to the evidence for increased hunting efficiency by the Neanderthals.

The use of flake knives is also to be seen in the Mousterian and can be taken to indicate the Neanderthals' increased concern with manipulating and shaping the natural world confronting them. This correlates with the increases in the problem of simple survival which the onset of the last glaciation must have imposed on human existence during the Neanderthal stage.

This last item raises issues of considerable importance to the archaeologist. Before the onset of the last (Würm) glaciation, the representatives of genus *Homo* were unable to cope with a subarctic environment. Consistent with his area of origin, man remains a physiologically tropical animal to this day; his ability to invade and exploit other environments is a product of specializations in his cultural adaptive mechanism. Until the late third interglacial, however, this cultural adaptive mechanism was not well enough developed to compensate for his physical inadequacies to the extent of allowing him to survive in a really chilly area. The onset of the preceding glaciations then forced people out of the increasingly inhospitable parts of what had formerly been the temperate zone. Climatic changes produced by the onset of glacial conditions were most extreme at the western end of the Old World temperate zone, where the Alps acted like an enormous refrigerator and cooled off the whole of Europe. Scandinavia added to this general chilling and contributed to the continental ice sheet, which moved south across the Baltic, blanketing the northern edge of continental Europe and much of the British Isles. Since the most extreme climatic changes in the Old World focussed at the European end of the range, it is reasonable to expect that the greatest population dislocations occurred there as well.

By the time of the onset of the Würm, however, the pre-Neanderthal level of cultural attainment was just high enough so that, with some modifications, it allowed people to remain in the more northern unglaciated parts of Europe, southern Russia, and the Middle East, and take advantage of the abundant food supply represented by the great numbers of large Pleistocene mammals which thrived there. Culturally this represents a kind of forced adaptation which took place in the western reaches of the north temperate zone, with the consequence that, for the first time since the

Australopithecine stage, there was a marked difference in the cultural adaptations of otherwise similar peoples in different parts of the world.

Archaeological evidence from Africa suggests that some of the technological inventions of the Mousterian culture area diffused to the south, where such things as spear points were made according to local techniques of manufacture, but the whole complex which bears the label Mousterian remained in the north. There are some suggestive tool fragments in China and Mongolia, but by-and-large it would appear that no such development occurred there or in India. Accident of circumstances, then, gave the inhabitants of the area from Europe through the Middle East a technological head start over the other peoples of the world, and, with many modifications, the effect of this fortuitous set of events continues to the present day.

As with the advance from the Australopithecine to the Pithecanthropine stages, the development from the Pithecanthropine to the Neanderthal stage took place throughout the inhabited parts of the Old World at the same time. This presents something of a contradiction if we use a strict interpretation of Mousterian in our definition of the Neanderthal stage, because of the limited geographical distribution of what is technically included within the term Mousterian. Some better cultural term should be used for the purpose of defining Neanderthal as a world-wide stage. Some archaeologists have used the term Middle Palaeolithic to differentiate it from the Upper and Lower Palaeolithic, and this term might be preferable were there not so much archaeological opposition. Perhaps the term "Mousterioid" might be used provisionally to include the Mousterian proper and all the similar cultures based on flake technology.

As an indicator of the geographical distribution of the Neanderthal stage, human skeletal material is almost better than the archaelogical record—far less complete of course, but more clearly indicative. The European skeletal material is represented by the original Neanderthaler, the Spy remains, the "Old man" of La Chapelle-aux-Saints, skeletal remains from La Ferrassie, Gibraltar, La Quina, Monte Circeo, and a great many more less complete finds. Relatively abundant remains have been discovered in southern Russia and the Middle East, with perhaps the most exciting (and datable) remains coming within the last decade from Shanidar cave in Iraq. The most complete skeleton is the female from the Tabūn cave on Mount Carmel in Palestine. Skeletal remains of the Neanderthal stage from the rest of the Old World are much less abundant, although the available fragments allow the inferences of distribution to be made.

In sub-Saharan Africa the famous Rhodesian skull, discovered in 1921 deep in a mine shaft, can serve as a representative of the African version

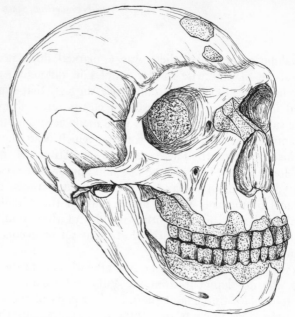

The "Old Man" from La Chapelle-aux-Saints, Correze, southwestern France. An extreme example of the "classic" Neanderthals.

of the Neanderthal stage. Unfortunately the evidence for its age is tenuous at best, although the physical characteristics are Neanderthal (in the extreme), in spite of attempts by some to regard it as hinting at the modern and by others to peg it as a full Pithecanthropine technically included within the species *Homo erectus*. Brain size is fully modern, if small

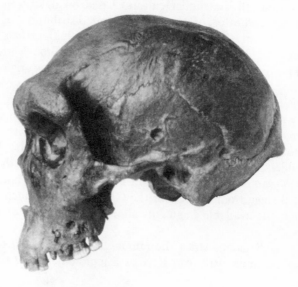

The Rhodesian skull, an African Neanderthal. (Courtesy of the American Museum of Natural History.)

One of the Solo skulls, a Javanese candidate for the Neanderthal stage. (Courtesy of the American Museum of Natural History, New York.)

modern (1,250 cc.), but the face, capped by a stupendous brow ridge, is Middle Pleistocene. Considering the discussion offered above, this should qualify the Rhodesian skull as a good potential Neanderthal.

Added confirmation for this appraisal, plus justification for regarding it as contemporary with the European Neanderthals, can be found in the discovery of a near twin only a scant hundred miles north of the Cape of Good Hope. This is the Saldanha skull, found in 1953 near Hopefield on Saldanha Bay, South Africa. Although lacking a face, the Saldanha skull is similar in every detail to the Rhodesian skull, and furthermore, it occurs with associated Mousterioid artifacts in an early Upper Pleistocene context. Even if this is not on a par with abundant evidence from Europe, the dating, the artifacts, and the form provide strong support for the inferences concerning the existence of the Neanderthal stage in Africa.

To complete the picture of Neanderthal distribution, the Far East has also obligingly yielded some crucial fossils. As with the initial discovery and the confirmation of the Pithecanthropine stage, Java has played the central role. Starting in 1931, 11 broken and faceless skulls were unearthed on the banks of the Solo River which recall the Pithecanthropines on the one hand and the Neanderthals on the other. The bones of the cranial vault are thick, the brow ridges and muscle markings are heavy, and the keeling along the mid-line, together with other details, looks more than faintly Pithecanthropine, but the cranial capacity is half way between Pithecanthropine and Neanderthal/modern. All told, the Solo skulls appear to represent an evolutionary transition from the Pithecanthropine to the Neanderthal stage in the Far East. Together with other more recent skeletal remains, the evidence is most suggestive that the stage-to-stage evolution occurred simultaneously in all parts of the inhabited world— Europe, Africa, Asia, and by inference the areas between. Further confirmation of a full Neanderthal in Asia is offered by the discovery in 1958 of the upper parts of the face and the forward part of a skull of good Neanderthal form at Mapa, some 300 miles north of Canton in China.

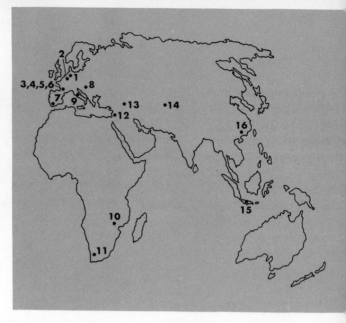

Neantherthal distribution as represented by the locations of some of the more important discoveries. 1. Neanderthal. 2. Spy. 3. La Chapelle-aux-Saints. 4. Le Moustier. 5. La Ferrassie. 6. La Quina. 7. Gibraltar. 8. Krapina. 9. Saccopastore. 10. Broken Hill (Rhodesian Man). 11. Saldanha. 12. Mount Carmel. 13. Shanidar. 14. Teshik Tash. 15. Solo. 16. Ma-Pa.

The foregoing should suffice to indicate the form, the dating, and the distribution of the Neanderthal stage. Since full modern cranial capacity had been attained, presumably indicating intellectual capabilities equivalent to those of modern man, it would not be justifiable to regard the Neanderthals as specifically distinct from men of today. Formally, then, this makes them *Homo sapiens* with at most a subspecific appendage of *Neanderthalensis*.

Twelve The Modern Stage

Forty years ago, the appearance of modern man would have been announced in phrases such as these: "Sweeping into Europe from out of the East came a new type of man, tall and straight, with strong but finely formed limbs, whose superiority is proclaimed in the smooth brow and lofty forehead, and whose firm and prominent chin bespeaks a mentality in no way inferior to that of ourselves. In this fine and virile race we can recognize our own ancestors who suddenly appear upon the scene and replace the degenerate and inferior Neanderthals, perhaps as a result of bloody conflict in which the superior mentality and physique of the newcomers tipped the balance. Whatever the cause, the lowly Neanderthals disappear forever and the land henceforth becomes the never-to-be-relinquished home of our own lineage, the creator of the culture which is our own patrimony, and the originator of what has been built to the heights of Western civilization."

While this paragraph is pure invention, it nevertheless captures some of the flavor of the interpretive accounts of human evolution written a half century ago. Their appeal to the imagination of the literate world was immense. In the first place, the reference to an Eastern origin strikes a powerful chord in the mind of the Western reader who is conditioned from infancy to regard all that is civilized and sanctified in antiquity to have had its origins "in the East."

To these holy overtones are added the implications of the mysterious Orient. But this is just the beginning. The appeal to the lofty brow, often accompanied by explicit statements concerning the degree of development of the frontal lobes of the brain, caters to a folk belief, dating from the phrenology of the early nineteenth century and still current, that this is somehow indicative of superior mental ability. The portrayal of our own ancestors in terms which correspond to the stereotyped picture of European masculinity—prominent chin, straight-limbed, tall, to which hints of blue eyes and fair hair are often added—stimulates a conscious pride in belonging to such a line. To complete the scene with all the components of a good old-fashioned melodrama, the Neanderthals are brought in as the embodiment of the villain. They are depicted as strong and dangerous, although dwarfed and physically inferior, crafty but not really intelligent, hairy and doubtless violent and bestial. In spite of adversities, good prevails

An Upper Palaeolithic hunter, *the first of the modern stage. Neatly dressed and clean shaven, he strides forth confidently to fulfill the destiny which his clear vision tells him is to be his future. Actually the archaeological evidence does provide support for the existence if not the invention of tailored clothing and compound weapons in the Upper Palaeolithic, but the lofty brow and "noble" expression are quite unwarranted idealizations.*

and evil is vanquished, with the Neanderthals disappearing forever.

As an added attraction to our already potent little drama, all direct relationship between the Neanderthals and the invading moderns is either flatly denied, or pushed so far back in time that it is lost in the mists of remote antiquity—which of course means that even people who are uneasy about accepting an evolutionary account of the origins of modern man can accept this story without any qualms. Dazzled by such dramatics, few people were disturbed by the total lack of any reason for such an invasion, of any source for the invaders, or of any perspectives on what they evolved out of and why. Analagous to the legend in which Athena sprang fully armed from the brow of Zeus, so it would seem that early twentieth-century prehistorians solved their headache concerning human origins by projecting modern man, fully formed, from their own inner consciousness smack into the early Pleistocene and thereby created their own anthropological mythology.

It scarcely needs to be said that this book does not subscribe to such a myth-like view. Recognizing that it is essentially an expression of faith—faith in a process—the attitude behind this presentation is based on the assumption that the hominid fossil record can be comfortably accommodated within the framework of standard evolutionary theory as it is applied to the human world. Noting that the Neanderthals have an antiquity demonstrably greater than that of modern man and that nothing but modern skeletal material is evident since about 35,000 years ago, it is important to place both stages within the same evolutionary framework. If, as is claimed, the Neanderthals evolved into modern men, then structurally and temporally intermediate forms should be apparent, and some rationale should be available to account for the change. Fortunately (for the present scheme), both can be produced.

In the early 1930's, excavations in the rock shelter of Skhūl on the slopes of Mount Carmel in Palestine (near the cave of Tabūn which yielded a full-scale Neanderthal) produced a population of what can be called **Neanderthaloids.** That is, they recall genuine Neanderthalers in many respects, but in other features deviate in the direction of modern men. The dentition and the entire surrounding face has been somewhat reduced, leaving the forehead and sides of the cranial vault more vertical and producing the first vestiges of a genuine chin—formerly regarded as the "hallmark" of modern man. Reductions in the robustness of ribs, long bones, and other aspects of the postcranial skeleton also show modification in the modern direction. For many years the suggestion was made that the Mount Carmel material was third interglacial, which would have made it older than the full Neanderthals dated to the fourth glaciation in Europe and recently confirmed at Shanidar in Iraq. To explain this mixture of traits, the interpretation was advanced that the people of Mount Carmel were hybrids between a fully Neanderthal group, represented by Tabūn and now Shanidar, and a fully modern group for which such vague fragments as Swanscombe or even the Piltdown fraud were advanced. Recently, however, the difficulties which such an approach encounters have been altered by the reappraisal of Mount Carmel dating. By C_{14}, the Tabūn skeleton has been shown to be only 41,000 years old, and the Skhūl material by projection is considered to be some 5,000 years more recent. This places the Skhūl population, which is intermediate in form, just half way between the Neanderthal and modern ends of a 10,000-year gap, and eliminates all need for theories involving hybridization, with their attendant difficulties.

Nor is the Skhūl population with its 10 individuals the only evidence for the existence of Neanderthaloids. At Krapina in Croatia (Yugoslavia) a similar population was discovered during the first half-decade of the twentieth century. Although the Krapina remains are badly fragmented, the picture they present is of a Neanderthaloid population closer to the Neanderthal than the modern end of the spectrum. They too had been formerly considered third interglacial, but recent stratigraphic work has equated them with an interstadial (amelioration) within the Würm glaciation, making their age about equivalent to the Skhūl Neanderthaloids.

A few other isolated finds of intermediate character also exist (the Rhünda skull found in Germany in 1956 and the Florisbad skull from South Africa in 1932), and the Neanderthal origin of modern man is further supported by the presence of a fair proportion of dissociated Nean-

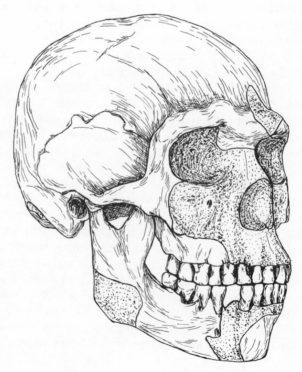

A *Neanderthaloid skull, Skhūl V, the best-preserved representative from a group of ten individuals found in a rock shelter on the slopes of Mount Carmel, Palestine, in the early 1930's.*

derthaloid characteristics in the earliest clearly Upper Palaeolithic populations. The first such Upper Palaeolithic population to be discovered was the Cro-Magnon group, found less than a decade after Darwin's *Origin* appeared. Occasionally the term Cro-Magnon is applied to designate the early moderns as a stage, and occasionally it and other terms (Grimaldi, Combe Capelle, Chancelade, etc.) are used to designate separate supposed "races" of modern people in the Upper Palaeolithic. This would seem premature, since it is even less likely that four or more separate races existed in southern France (where these representatives were found) during the Upper Palaeolithic than that Australopithecines and Pithecanthropines were contemporaries in South Africa or Java at an earlier date. For the present, these can all be referred to as the Upper Palaeolithic representatives of the Modern stage. As has already been mentioned, the chief physical differences between the Neanderthals and the moderns is to be seen in the development of the dentition, its supporting facial architecture, and related parts of the skull plus certain aspects of general skeletal development and musculature. In all these features, the moderns show a marked degree of reduction from the Neanderthal state, although the early Upper Palaeolithic representatives are markedly more robust in these features than is generally true for modern man today.

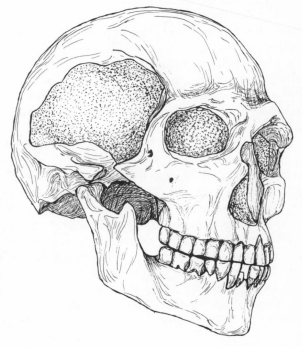

An Upper Palaeolithic skull, Předmost III, a male from a large collection excavated in western Czechoslovakia in the late nineteenth and early twentieth centuries. A lingering robustness of brow ridges, facial skeleton, and muscle markings recall earlier conditions in human evolution.

Several generations of scholars have noted that the appearance of modern form is correlated with the appearance of Upper Palaeolithic tool-making traditions which represent an advance in complexity over the Mousterian comparable to the advance which the Mousterian showed over the Lower Palaeolithic. Refinements in tool-making are signalled by the technique of preparing flint cores so that long narrow spalls, technically called **blades**, can be detached. This increases the number of tools which a given amount of raw material can yield, and, further, the tools thus produced are worked into a greater variety of functionally distinct forms than was previously the case. Points, knives, and scrapers are refined, and to these are added a variety of gouging tools called **burins**. Also notable is the appearance of an extensive bone industry—harpoon points, awls, and needles with eyes in them. With the small flint spear points and harpoon heads, it is apparent that hunting now definitely uses the technique of hurling projectiles at prey. This is further supported by the appearance of spear-throwers, **atlatls**, which, by acting as an extension of the arm, significantly increases the power of propulsion and adds to the effective range over which a spear can operate. Certainly the vast quantities of animal remains found in Upper Palaeolithic sites attest to the effectiveness of hunting techniques, and one can assume that a higher level of social cooperation in game drives and trapping procedures must have existed as well. Finally, from the needles it has been inferred that shaped and sewn—tailored—clothing was being made.

Initially the Upper Palaeolithic appears in the same area where the Mousterian had flourished before it. The same caves are utilized as shelters and the same kinds of animals are being hunted. All told, it can be regarded as a refined outgrowth—a culminating perfection—of the cold-climate adaptation of which the Mousterian represents the beginning. New technological items have been added, although many are simply refinements of the cruder Mousterian counterparts, but the basic dimensions of life are not radically different. The difference is more one of relative efficiency than of kind.

Survival in the north temperate zone depended upon the cultural developments which started in the Mousterian and continued without break in the Upper Palaeolithic. Since cultural changes, even at the Australopithecine level, represent alterations in the selective forces which affect the hominids involved, one should expect to find some sort of reflected change to have occurred in the anatomy of the beneficiaries. One of the most obvious differences which set apart the Mousterian and the Upper Palaeolithic from the preceding Lower Palaeolithic is the appearance of a profusion of special cutting tools. From the **bifaces** (hand axes) and crude flakes of the pre-Würm cultures one goes to the variety of points, scrapers,

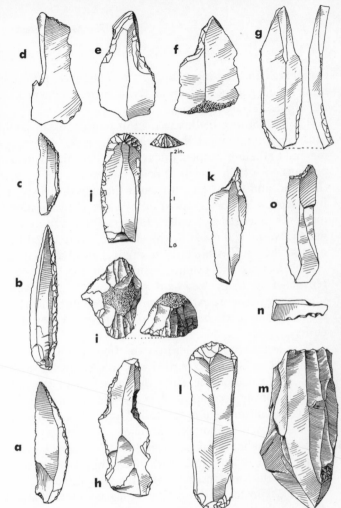

Upper Palaeolithic flint tools. a and b, "knife points"; d, e, f, and g, gravers or burins; i, j, l, and o, scrapers; k, a piercer; c, h, and n, miscellaneous tools; m, a core from which blades have been struck. (By permission of the Trustees of the British Museum, [Natural History].)

and knives of the Mousterian and the even more elaborate technology of the Upper Palaeolithic. Obviously the ability to manipulate the world around him has been one of the prime factors in the successful survival of the creature man, but equally obvious is the fact that a technological basis for any extensive manipulating did not exist prior to the Mousterian.

From the extraordinary wear visible on the front teeth of the Neanderthals and their predecessors, one can suggest that it was the dentition which bore the brunt of the finer manipulations and itself served as a sort of general all-purpose tool—the original built-in. With the appearance of an adequate cutlery at the beginning of the Mousterian, the significance of possessing large and powerful front teeth was substantially decreased. This would have allowed the probable mutation effect to operate throughout the early Würm, resulting in the reduction of the forward part of the dental arch and the supporting parts of the face. Furthermore, the process must have been speeded up as technological refinement advanced toward the Upper Palaeolithic level.

The significance of this change in tooth use can be appreciated if one considers for a moment the characteristic mode of eating of modern hunting and gathering peoples. Meat is not daintily manicured into bite-sized portions with knife and fork before ingesting; rather, a chunk is taken in the hand and thrust part way into the mouth, where it is held with the front teeth while being sawed off at lip level by means of a cutting implement. As practiced by modern hunters and a variety of peasants throughout the world, it is aided by the efficiency represented by metal knives, but even so the effect is sufficient to produce a substantial amount of flat wear on the incisors and canines, resulting in the "edge-to-edge" bite characteristic of so many backward peoples. Before metallurgy, this form of tooth wear was more extensive, and one can just imagine the burden placed on the front teeth *before* the development of even an adequate *stone* cutlery.

The heavy wear apparent on the front teeth of many of the Neanderthals indicates that the burden was only gradually shifted from the dentition. This is reasonable, since the reduction of the full Neanderthal face is only halfway accomplished in the Skhūl population of Mount Carmel and is still incomplete in the early Upper Palaeolithic, and it suggests that the teeth were important for more than simply processing food. The curious rounding wear of Neanderthal incisors indicates that they were using their teeth to tan leather in a fashion similar to that of the modern Eskimo, which is consistent with the view presented above that they were utilizing skins for clothing. This brings up another area of cultural adaptation which leads to another suggestive if unproven speculation.

Recall that the development of a hairless and heavily pigmented skin was suggested for the hunters early in the Pithecanthropine stage. From this, one must assume that the early Neanderthals who first successfully adapted to the north temperate zone in the early Würm were dark brown or "black," as a correlate to man's generally tropical physiology. The use of clothing, among other things, was of great importance in the success of their adaptation, but one can suggest that it had an interesting if somewhat unexpected by-product. By covering the skin with clothes, the importance of the epidermal pigment melanin as an ultraviolet filter is drastically reduced, and, once again, the probable mutation effect operating over a substantial period of time would serve to reduce the structure whose importance had been decreased. The result is depigmentation, and it is of more than passing interest to note that, in general, those parts of the world where the amount of pigment in the human skin is at a minimum are also just those areas where Mousterian scrapers and Neanderthal teeth indicate that clothing has been utilized for the longest period of time. The picture evoked by a blond Neanderthaler is somewhat contrary to the usual stereotype, but it is quite possible that the invention of clothing by the northern Neanderthals of the early Würm was the source of the depigmentation phenomenon which allows some of the peoples of the world today to be described by the euphemism "white."

With changes in man's cultural adaptive mechanism suggested as being responsible for changes in face form and skin color, it should be possible to account for some of the major visible differences between the living peoples of the world in the same way, and this is indeed the case, although to go into this in any detail is beyond the scope of this book. If the mechanisms discussed above have validity, then it is not unexpected to discover that the zone extending from the central part of western Europe through the Middle East contains people with the smallest teeth relative to gross body size of anywhere in the world. After all, this is just the area where the cultural advance took place which enabled man to remain in the north temperate zone during the chilling of the fourth glaciation. In the area where technological complexity has been having its impact for the greatest length of time, one would expect dental reduction to have proceeded to its greatest extent—and, as can be seen, these expectations are fulfilled. Using the same logic, one would expect the different degrees of dental development seen in India, Africa, Asia, the Americas, and Australia to be correlated with the length of time during which the relevant peoples have been enjoying the benefits of technological elaboration—and, again, expectations are fulfilled. The most striking example is that of Australia, where the facial form of the aborigines is remarkably similar to that of the Neanderthaloids of Mount Carmel, and where technological elaboration is more comparable to the Mousterian than to the European Upper Palaeolithic.

Using the arguments developed above, one can suggest that the human diversity visible in the world today is largely a product of events which have occurred during the last 70,000 years or so. It is only during this time that the archaeological record yields clear signs of functional differentiation in man's cultural adaptive mechanism. This, as has been suggested, was initiated by the survival problems posed by the periglacial areas. Solution of these had a number of important consequences. One of these was the ability to thrive in the more northern areas which were opened up during retreats of the ice sheets. Following these north, people at the Upper Palaeolithic level spread across the whole vast plains area of the Old World and, at the eastern extremity, crossed the land bridge between Siberia and Alaska, producing the initial population of the New World— the only large-scale spread into previously unoccupied territory to have occurred since the expansion of the *Paranthropus* phase throughout the

Old World tropics. It was people at a developed level of this same general stage of complexity who were able to domesticate plants and animals, thus assuring their food sources and creating the foundation for the still greater cultural disparities which followed. (This food producing or Neolithic revolution occurred about 10,000 years ago in the Middle East and, independently, somewhat more recently in Middle America). The effects of these various developments slowly diffused into other parts of the world, but a detailed discussion of the events involved and their impact is the subject of other books in this series.

One is tempted to speculate that the increasing technical and medical ingenuity of developing world culture will further reduce or suspend the adaptive significance of many other human features. Reduction of these features as a result of the probable mutation effect would then follow, and it is possible to suggest that the man of the future will be somewhat puny and underendowed by today's standards. Each era creates its own values, however, and the Neanderthals might very well have had the same feelings about ourselves, could they have known that we their remote descen-

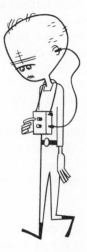

The man of the future (*we are tempted to call him* Homo durabilis *or the man who endures.*) *Although it is perhaps unwarranted to visualize our distant descendants as puny, balding, myopic, and toothless little men, yet there is reason to suspect that some such trends may occur. Note that in the previous stages of human evolution the cultural element symbolizing human adaptation was held in the hand of the man in question whereas in this portrayal it is hung around his neck.*

dants should be so much less robust than they. Perhaps our hypothetical man of 1,000,000 A.D.—should we call him *Homo durabilis*, "the man who endures"—will look back at the people of the twentieth century with feelings of repugnance and disgust. Tempting as such excursions may be, they do not properly belong in a book about man's past. In fact, they hardly belong to the realm of "science," and are included here only to lead the reader to realize that human evolution is not just something that occurred long ago—that it has been continual, that it is happening right now, and that it will go on in the future as long as man shall exist.

Epilogue

In summary, the figure below presents a supersimplified picture of the changes which have occurred in the entire span of human evolution, with their suggested causes. From the Paranthropus phase onward, the changes in brain, molar, and incisor size reflect the main events, but to properly include the early Australopithecines, one must remember that they were about half the bulk of the later stages, so that mental corrections have to be made for the proportionate sizes of these several organs.

It does not take an expert to recognize that more than the usual amount of speculation has been included in this book. The major pieces of evidence have been presented, and evolutionary theory has been considered. The speculation enters when theory rather than solid evidence has been used to support the interpretations offered, and it should be clearly recognized that this cannot constitute proof. As more fragments of human fossils are found in the years to come, the level of probability that one interpretation or another is correct will increase, but this too is not proof. Ultimately it is impossible to "prove" the validity of any interpretation,

but the theoretical consistency of the one presented here should be justification enough for its development. The future alone can decide the
probability of its rectitude.

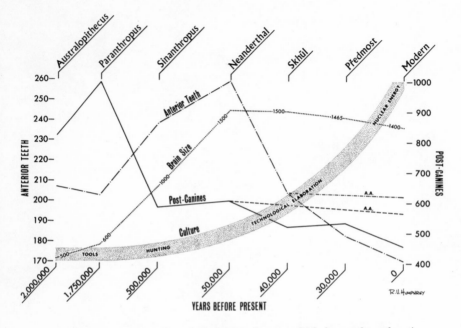

Graphic representation of the major changes which have taken place in
human evolution and their association with changes in man's cultural
adaptation. The figures for anterior teeth and post-canines represent the
summed cross-section area of the teeth on one side of the upper dental
arch. Brain size is in cubic centimeters. A. A. refers to modern Australian
aborigines—note how close they are to the Neanderthaloids from Skhūl,
Mount Carmel.

Selected References

Chapter One

There are a few books that will serve as background for interpretations of human evolution. The most complete and systematic of these is *Catalogue des Hommes Fossiles*, H. V. Vallois and H. L. Movius, eds. (Macon: Protat Frères, 1953). A more recent, well illustrated, but incomplete source is Michael H. Day's *Guide to Fossil Man: A Handbook of Human Palaeontology* (Cleveland and New York: The World Publishing Company, 1965). An excellent discussion, although a very orthodox presentation, is available in W. E. Le Gros Clark's *The Fossil Evidence for Human Evolution: An Introduction to the Study of Paleoanthropology*, 2nd ed. (Chicago: University of Chicago Press, 1964). Dating of the evidence is treated in Kenneth P. Oakley's *Frameworks for Dating Fossil Man*, 2nd ed. (Chicago: Aldine Publishing Company, 1966).

Chapter Two

The background for the development of evolutionary thought is well portrayed by John C. Greene in *The Death of Adam: Evolution and its Impact on Western Thought* (Ames: The Iowa State University Press, 1959). The triumph of the Darwinian point of view is well developed in Loren C. Eiseley's *Darwin's Century: Evolution and the Men Who Discovered It* (Garden City: Doubleday & Company, Inc., 1958).

To gain some background in the attitudes of the French intellectual climate where Darwinian evolution has been resisted, see William Coleman, *Georges Cuvier, Zoologist* (Cambridge: Harvard University Press, 1964). This provides valuable perspective for understanding the interpretations offered in one of the widely used reference sources for human evolution, *Fossil Men*, by M. Boule and H. V. Vallois (New York: Dryden Press, 1957).

Chapter Three

The first and still one of the best attempts to interpret the skeletal remains of prehistoric human populations from a systematically evolutionary point of view is *Studien zur Vorgeschichte des Menschen* by Gustav Schwalbe (Stuttgart: E. Scheizerbart, 1906). Probably the best account of early discoveries and interpretations in English is Aleš Hrdlička's *The Skeletal Remains of Early Man*, Smithsonian Miscellaneous Collections No. 83 (Washington, D.C.: The Smithsonian Institution, 1930).

Chapter Four

The only explicit attempt to consider the impact of national intellectual traditions and the accidents of history on the interpretation of the evidence for human evolution is in "The fate of the 'classic' Neanderthals: A consideration of hominid catastrophism," by C. L. Brace in *Current Anthropology*, V, No. 1 (1964). Particularly interesting are the irate comments of the proponents of the traditional view which are printed following the main body of the article. This provides the basis for the view presented in Chapter VI of C. L. Brace and M. F. Ashley Montagu's *Man's Evolution: An Introduction to Physical Anthropology* (New York: The Macmillan Company, 1965). For further repercussions, see the review of the preceding work by Robert W. Ehrich in *Human Biology*, XXXVIII, No. 3 (1966), and "More on the fate of the 'classic' Neanderthals," *Current Anthropology*, VII, No. 2 (1966).

Chapter Five

The accounts of those who contributed to the discoveries are particularly interesting. Franz Weidenreich reported some of his conclusions in *Apes, Giants and Man* (Chicago: The University of Chicago Press, 1946), but the most complete personal account is presented by G. H. R. von Koenigswald in *Meeting Prehistoric Man* (London: Thames & Hudson, 1956).

Chapter Six

Although some of the interpretations have been generally questioned, the most complete account to have been published of discoveries up to 1962 is Carleton S. Coon's *The Origin of Races* (New York: Alfred A. Knopf, 1962). For still more recent material, see

William Howells' *Mankind in the Making: The Story of Human Evolution*, revised ed. (Garden City: Doubleday & Company, Inc., 1967).

Chapter Seven
Standard evolutionary principles are well expressed in such relatively recent works as *Introduction to Evolution*, 2nd ed., by Paul Amos Moody, (New York: Harper and Brothers, 1962) and *Animal Species and Evolution* by Ernst Mayr (Cambridge: The Belknap Press of the Harvard University Press, 1963), although the best exposition is still probably that found in an older work by George Gaylord Simpson, *The Major Features of Evolution* (New York: Columbia University Press, 1953).

Reflecting the revolutionary developments which occurred in genetics starting fifteen years ago, a good early synthesis of some of the implications can be found in *The Molecular Basis of Evolution* by Christian B. Anfinsen (New York: John Wiley & Sons, Inc., 1959). Capitalizing on these developments, and suggested as being of particular importance to human evolution, is the paper by C. L. Brace, "Structural Reduction in Evolution," *The American Naturalist*, XCVII, No. 1 (1963).

Chapter Eight
One of the earliest explicit realizations of the behavioral significance of hominid body form was the unappreciated paper by Paul Alsberg, "The Taungs Puzzle: a Biological Essay," *Man*, XXXIV, No. 179, (1934).

For specific treatment of hominid ecology, tool use, behavior, and cultural adaptation, the following three papers overlap to provide a coherent picture: G. A. Bartholomew and J. B. Birdsell, "Ecology and the Protohominids," *American Anthropologist*, LV, No. 4 (1953); Marshall D. Sahlins, "The Origin of Society," *Scientific American*, CCIII, No. 3 (1960); and S. L. Washburn, "Tools and Human Evolution," *Scientific American*, CCIII, No. 3 (1960).

Chapter Nine
The initial modest paper of R. A. Dart, remarkable for the furor which it touched off, is still worth reading: "*Australopithecus africanus*: The Man-ape of South Africa," *Nature*, CXV (February 7, 1925). Professor Dart's personal involvement with Australopithecine research is depicted in *Adventures with the Missing Link* by R. A. Dart and Dennis Craig (New York: Harper and Brothers, 1959).

Describing the variety of Australopithecine material, the paper by J. T. Robinson, "The Genera and Species of the Australopithecinae," *American Journal of Physical Anthropology*, XII, No. 2 (1954) represents an early synthesis. The major work on the one easily quantifiable aspect of the Australopithecines, the teeth, is also by J. T. Robinson, *The Dentition of the Australopithecinae*, Transvaal Museum Memoirs, No. 9 (Pretoria, 1956).

For various points of view on the most recent discoveries in East Africa and their interpretations, one should read the collection of papers by Evernden and Curtis, L. S. B. Leakey, P. V. Tobias and G. H. R. von Koenigswald and others, published as a collection entitled "The Origin of Man," *Current Anthropology*, VI, No. 4 (1965).

The most recent assessment of Australopithecine problems is by the usually conservative W. E. Le Gros Clark, *Man-Apes or Ape-Men?* (New York: Holt, Rinehart and Winston, Inc., 1967).

Chapter Ten
For the Pithecanthropines, the standard reference against which all accounts are compared is Franz Weidenreich's "The Skull of *Sinanthropus pekinensis*," *Palaeontologia Sinica*, X (1943). Presenting a more historically oriented picture is G. H. R. von Koenigswald's "The discovery of Early Man in Java and Southern China," in *Early Man in the Far East*, W. W. Howells, ed., Studies in Physical Anthropology, No. 1 (American Association of Physical Anthropologists, 1949).

For an appraisal of the most recently discovered Pithecanthropines, see William Howells' "*Homo erectus*," *Scientific American*, CCXV, No. 5 (1966).

Chapter Eleven
Many if not most physical anthropologists prefer the approach to the Neanderthal problem represented in the writings of F. Clark Howell, for instance in "The Place of Neanderthal Man in Human Evolution," *American Journal of Physical Anthropology*, IX, No. 4 (1951); and "The Evolutionary Significance of Variation and Varieties of 'Neanderthal' Man," *Quarterly Review of Biology*, XXXII, No. 4 (1957). For a collection of papers generally in the traditional frame of reference, see *Hundert Jahre Neanderthaler: Neanderthal Centenary*, G. H. R. von Koenigswald, ed. (Utrecht: Kemink en Zoon, 1959).

A rather different view is presented by C. L. Brace in "Refocussing on the Neanderthal Problem," *American Anthropologist*, LXIV, No. 4 (1962).

Chapter Twelve
Comprehensive treatments of modern human physical development are represented by widely differing but mutually complementing approaches, for instance Theodosius Dobzhansky, *Mankind Evolving* (New Haven: Yale University Press, 1962); and Bernard G. Campbell, *Human Evolution: An Introduction to Man's Adaptation* (Chicago: Aldine Publishing Co., 1966).

A relatively standard treatment of contemporary human variation is seen in Carleton S. Coon's *The Living Races of Man*, (New York: Alfred A. Knopf, 1965).

A less popular approach is taken by C. L. Brace in "A Non-racial Approach toward the Understanding of Human Diversity," in *The Concept of Race*, M. F. Ashley Montagu, ed. (New York: The Free Press of Glencoe, 1964); see also Part III in Brace and Montagu, *Man's Evolution* (New York: The Macmillan Company, 1965).

Index

113